RAMESSES THE GREAT

CHARLOTTE

Presented by the Mint Museum of Art
in cooperation with
the Egyptian Antiquities Organization

Rita E. Freed

RAMESSES
THE GREAT

THE PHARAOH AND HIS TIM

MINT MUSEUM OF ART · CHARLOTTE, N.

First printing
Ramesses the Great, an exhibition in the city of Memphis

Project Coordinator: Nancy E. Bogatin
Graphic Design: Polly Sexton
Editor: Liz Conway
Consulting Editor: Carol Lynn Yellin
Contributing Editor: Valerie Moore
Technical Editors: Anna Kay Walker, Lynn Gibson
Index Compilation: Catherine C. Swearingen
Color Separations and Printing: Lithograph Printing Company
Typography: Marcol Graphics of Memphis

This exhibition is supported by an indemnity from the
Federal Council on the Arts and Humanities.

Fourth printing
Ramesses the Great: The Pharaoh and His Time, an
exhibition at the Mint Museum of Art, Charlotte, N.C.
October 1, 1988-January 31, 1989

Project Director: Milton J. Bloch
Project Coordinator: Robert E. Bush, Jr.
Curator and Publications Coordinator: Charles L. Mo
Exhibition Designer: Daniel P. Gottlieb
Color Separations and Printing: Lithograph Printing Company
Typography: Marcol Graphics of Memphis

The Mint Museum of Art is sponsored by the City of
Charlotte, the Arts and Science Council of
Charlotte/Mecklenburg and is a Statewide Arts
Resource of the North Carolina Arts Council.

Library of Congress Cataloging-in-Publication Data
Freed, Rita E.
    Ramesses the Great: the pharaoh and his time

    "Presented by the Mint Museum of Art
in cooperation with the
Egyptian Antiquities Organization."
    Bibliography: p.
    Includes index.
    1. Egypt—Antiquities—Exhibitions. 2. Ramses II,
King of Egypt.   3. Egypt—Civilization—To 332 B.C.
I. Mint Museum of Art (Charlotte, N.C.)   II. Hayʾat
al-Āthaʾr al-Miṣriyah. III. Title.
DT59.B598F74 1988   932ʹ014ʹ0924   88-2605

Contents

R amesses the Great! The name has an awe-inspiring, mystical quality. This mighty pharaoh is among that elite group of historical figures whose name and accomplishments, rather than diminished by the passage of time, are enhanced with each succeeding century. That mystique, timelessness and grandeur is now apparent in the Ramesses the Great exhibition at the Mint Museum in Charlotte.

This breathtaking exhibition at the Mint Museum culminates more than two years of work that included negotiating with Egyptian government and museum officials, soliciting local underwriters, upfitting the Mint's facilities to display the exhibition adequately, and making the countless logistical arrangements necessary to accommodate an anticipated 450,000 visitors.

Obviously, none of this would have been possible without the cooperation of the Egyptian officials. Just as clearly, this exhibition never would have appeared in Charlotte but for the efforts of the Mint Museum board and staff. And certainly, all preliminary efforts would have gone for naught, had local companies and individuals not stepped forward to underwrite the exhibition.

In its historical significance and its artistic value, Ramesses the Great is enormously important in and of itself. By several measures, it ranks as the Mint's most ambitious undertaking ever.

In terms of its impact on the reputation of the Mint and the city of Charlotte, its significance is immeasurable. As one of the few U.S. locations honored to host the exhibition, the Mint will achieve a level of recognition that will pay dividends for years to come.

In brief, the magnitude and significance of this event gives Charlotte's Mint Museum of Art a prominent position on the nation's cultural map. Viewed in that light, all those whose efforts have made the Ramesses the Great exhibition a reality have created a new standard of achievement for both the Mint and the city. For that, they deserve our sincere gratitude.

On behalf of everyone involved in this exciting, enormous effort, welcome to Ramesses the Great: The Pharaoh and His Time.

James W. Thompson
President
Mint Museum of Art

A Message from the Minister of Culture of Egypt

The Ramesses the Great exhibition, with its varied treasures and monumental sculptures, provides the American people with an excellent opportunity to better understand the artistic craftsmanship and scientific knowledge of the ancient Egyptian; with a special focus on Ramesses II as man, god-king, and a ruler in whose reign the first recorded peace treaty in history occurred with the Hittites.

Ramesses the Great was a mighty pharaoh who enjoyed a long and prosperous reign. He was responsible for numerous building projects and commemorated his greatness with the construction of temples, chapels and statuary throughout the land. Even today, new discoveries in Egypt continue to reveal the name of this mighty king.

This exhibition is truly unique in that it not only supplies knowledge about Ramesses the Great, but also about the Ramesside period in ancient Egypt. This period witnessed the zenith of achievements in excellence in sculpture, architecture, astronomy and art.

Being an artist myself, I recognize within the artworks included in this exhibition marvelous aesthetic and philosophical statements provided by these ancient Egyptian artists. For example, within the monumental sculpture of Ramesses as a child with the falcon god, Hauron, the artist has provided a visual pun on the name Ramesses. Such ingenuity is worthy of pride in one's heritage. As Minister of Culture, I am also proud that this exhibition of over seventy treasures marks a continuation of the history of cultural relations between the Egyptian and American people.

Such a relationship is further strengthened by the educational benefits provided by such an exhibition. The exhibit with its variety of media and scale demonstrates the wealth of ancient Egyptian technology. It is interesting to consider that as the exhibition now tours the United States, modern Egyptian and American technology work together in all aspects associated with its presentation. I am confident that the people of Charlotte and its region will benefit from this presentation. It is but yet another link which strengthens the bond of friendship and understanding between the citizens of our two countries.

His Excellency Farouk Hosni
Minister of Culture of the Arab
Republic of Egypt
Cairo, Egypt

A Message from the Ambassador of Egypt

This important cultural occasion will present the opportunity to millions of Americans, I hope, to embark upon a thrilling adventure breaking free of the boundaries of time and space. The Ramesses exhibition on the one hand has the mystical effect of taking us back in time, to contemplate—even relive—a glorious period in human history and culture thousands of years ago. On the other hand, this exhibition will acquaint many Americans—perhaps for the first time—with Egyptian culture and history, so vital for the understanding of modern Egypt.

The historical importance of Ramesses II is undisputed, as a ruler who has left a legacy of greatness for which he will be eternally remembered. A brave man in war as well as in peace, the first recorded peace treaty in history which he made with the King of the Hittites is a certain tribute to his statemanship.

The monuments he left behind in Karnak, Luxor and Abu Simbel, attest to his taste for the grandiose and eternal as well as his love for a woman, Nefertari, his wife, for whom he built the temple of Hathor in Abu Simbel.

Nothing is more rewarding for one whose vocation it is to promote Egyptian-American relations and understanding than to see these beautiful statues and artifacts touring the United States, representing Egypt's spirit, and conveying a message of friendship.

The previous exhibits in Provo, Jacksonville, Memphis, Denver and Boston proved to be an unqualified success, engendering enthusiasm and leaving behind deep feelings of warmth and goodwill. The exhibition, at the Mint Museum in Charlotte, will—I am confident—take this success to even greater heights.

El Sayed Abdel Raouf El Reedy
The Ambassador of Egypt
Washington, D.C.

Egyptian Honorary Committee

Under the distinguished patronage
of His Excellency Mr. Hosni Mubarak
President of the Arab Republic of Egypt

His Excellency Dr. Aten Mohamed Naguib Sidki
The Prime Minister of the Arab Republic of Egypt

His Excellency Ahmed Esmat Abdel Meguid
The Minister of Foreign Affairs and
Deputy Prime Minister of the Arab Republic of Egypt

His Excellency Farouk Hosni
The Minister of Culture of the Arab Republic of Egypt

His Excellency El Sayed Abdel Raouf El Reedy
Ambassador of the Arab Republic of Egypt
to the United States of America

His Excellency Fouad El-Orabi
The First Under Secretary of State—
Ministry of Culture

His Excellency Mohammed Salmawy
Under Secretary of State for Foreign Affairs—
Ministry of Culture

Professor Dr. Gamal Mokhtar
The Former Director of the Egyptian Antiquities
Organization and Member of its Board of Directors

Professor Dr. Abdel Haliem Nour El Din
Director General of Egyptian Museums of the
Egyptian Antiquities Organization

Mr. Mohamed Ahmed Mohsen
Director General of the Egyptian Museum, Cairo

Dr. Zahi Hawass
Director General of Giza Pyramids and Sakkara,
Consultant of the Ministry of Culture for Archeology

Egyptian Organizing Committee

Mr. Mohamed Ahmed Mohsen
Director General of the Egyptian Museum, Cairo

Mrs. Saneya Abdel-Aal
Deputy Director of the Egyptian Museum, Cairo

Mr. Galal Sharawy
Deputy Director of the Egyptian Museum, Cairo

A Message from the Governor of the State of North Carolina

My compliments to the Mint Museum of Art, Charlotte for hosting the art exhibition of Ramesses the Great: The Pharaoh and His Time. This event will give the citizens of Charlotte and Mecklenburg County an opportunity to see a priceless collection of ancient Egyptian artifacts. The Mint Museum of Art is fortunate to be one of the few American hosts, to date, to present this exhibition to its visitors. I am sure that many North Carolinians will visit the museum from October 1, 1988 to January 31, 1989 to view over 70 objects dating back to over 1,000 B.C.

The exhibition will give students of Mecklenburg County and North Carolina a chance to learn about the culture and history of ancient Egypt. The educational importance of the artifacts equals their unique beauty. Our state will always remember the auspicious occasion when the Mint museum hosted this famous exhibition.

James G. Martin
Governor
State of North Carolina

A Message from the Mayor of Charlotte

Greetings!

It is very exciting for Charlotte's Mint Museum of Art to host the magnificent exhibition of Ramesses the Great, the most powerful king of ancient Egypt.

The opportunity to view the colossal Ramesses II statue and the spectacular collection of Egyptian treasures is truly an experience of a lifetime.

Because the exhibition is not expected to visit the United States again, Charlotte is proud to be a part of this North American tour.

Sue Myrick
Mayor of Charlotte

A Statement from the Chairman of the Ramesses Steering Committee

Colossal—Historic—Unique. The great civilization of ancient Egypt reaches out to the people of Charlotte and our world through the exhibition Ramesses the Great: The Pharaoh and His Time.

Though separated by over 3,000 years, we feel the enduring greatness of this man who claimed to be a god. We also see, like the poet Shelley, the pharaoh's humanity. Ramesses' pursuit of immortality may have been thwarted by "the lone and level sands," but he surely still lives in the minds of those who attend this exhibition. For this opportunity the Board of Trustees of the Mint Museum of Art expresses its sincere appreciation to the leadership of the Egyptian Antiquities Organization and His Excellency El Sayad Abdel Raouf El Reedy, Ambassador from Egypt.

We also thank the exhibition's underwriters and sponsors, the Woman's Auxiliary, those who served on special committees and the over three thousand volunteers who have made this event possible. For over 18 months, the Ramesses Steering Committee worked tirelessly with the Mint staff to develop and oversee the business plan for the exhibition. The Board wishes to thank committee members Patty Dewey, John Fielder, Karen Sachsenmaier, Zach Smith, and Jim Thompson for their steadfast dedication to this project. Finally, we extend a special debt of gratitude to Edwin Jones for bringing this opportunity to our attention and his instrumental role in assembling the financial underwriting for the exhibition; to Milton Bloch for guiding this endeavor to a successful completion, and to the staff of the Mint for their dedication, professionalism and tireless efforts.

On behalf of all those who have been involved in this historic undertaking, welcome to Ramesses the Great: The Pharaoh and His Time.

Thomas Cox, Jr.
Past President and
Chairman, Ramesses Steering Committee

A Statement from the Project Director

Ramesses the Great: The Pharaoh and His Time is probably the largest single public attraction ever presented in the Carolinas. It is more than an exhibition—it is an exercise in international cooperation, a model of community support, a study in planning and logistics, and a test of endurance and commitment. It is also a boon to Charlotte's economy, a priceless adjunct to the classroom studies of thousands of schoolchildren and a source of wonder and enjoyment for countless visitors.

As with the monumental works of Ramesses II, the exhibition is a heroic undertaking involving and requiring assistance from all quarters of our community. Underwriting for the exhibition was a community-wide effort with forty-three corporations, businesses, foundations and individuals insuring the funding for the exhibition and assuming the financial risks. The Charlotte Arts and Science Council gave its full support and also joined the group of underwriters, adding its financial backing as well. In addition to the underwriters, more than two dozen companies and individuals contributed money, services or goods which were instrumental to the project's success. The City of Charlotte assisted with the planning of signage, security and traffic control. Television stations and newspapers made special trips to Egypt to augment their extraordinary coverage of the event. Special promotions on behalf of the exhibition were conducted by the media and many area corporations. The Air National Guard assisted with the air-arrival of the exhibition artifacts. Ramesses the Great was chosen as the cover theme for over a million area telephone books. The Charlotte Convention and Visitors Bureau promoted the exhibition in every imaginable way. The North Carolina State Legislature made a generous contribution of free tickets for schoolchildren. EgyptAir, official airline for the exhibition, provided travel for all Egyptian participants and for the Mint staff. In addition, the staffs of the other hosting museums in Provo, Jacksonville, Memphis, Denver and Boston freely shared their experience and advice.

The Mint Museum trustees supported and endorsed the exhibition with great enthusiasm, while the staff outdid itself to measure up to the colossal undertaking. Over thirty additional staff were added and more than 3,000 people volunteered to help present and facilitate the exhibition. The Mint's auxiliaries supplied volunteers, and dozens of businessmen and enthusiastic residents joined numerous committees to facilitate the exhibition.

I cannot begin to offer adequate thanks to all the wonderful people who played such essential roles in this production. And, of course, my deepest appreciation goes to the Egyptian government for making the exhibition available. Special thanks to the Egyptian Antiquities Organization, the Egyptian Museum, Cairo, and to all the Egyptian governmental officials and museum experts who guided our efforts. All in all, I believe Ramesses himself would have been proud of the grand reception he has received in Charlotte.

Milton J. Bloch
Executive Director
Mint Museum of Art

Underwriters and Contributors

UNDERWRITERS

Duke Power Company Foundation
First Union Corporation
NCNB Corporation

The Dickson Foundation, Inc.
Ivey's
Mr. and Mrs. Edwin L. Jones, Jr.
The Knight Publishing Company, Inc.
Pepsi Cola Bottling Co. of
    Charlotte, Inc.
Southern Bell
Wachovia Bank and Trust Company, Inc.

Piedmont Natural Gas Company, Inc.

Belk Brothers Company
Mr. and Mrs. H. C. Bissel
Mr. and Mrs. John William Harris
Jefferson-Pilot Communications
    Company—WBTV, WBT, WBCY
Lance, Inc.
Royal Insurance Company
Sandoz Chemicals Corporation
Stephen R. Walsh

Arts and Science Council—Charlotte/
    Mecklenburg, Inc.
B B & T
BarclaysAmerican/Foundation, Inc.
The Blumenthal Foundation
Charlotte Pipe and Foundry Company
Collier Cobb & Associates, Inc.
The Equitable Financial Companies
Henry J. Faison
First Citizens Bank and Trust Company
Dr. and Mrs. E. Reed Gaskin
Ivan C. Hinrichs
Republic Bank & Trust Company
Trammell Crow Company
Young Ford, Inc.
United Carolina Bank

Arthur Andersen & Co.
Mr. and Mrs. William M. Barnhardt
The Franklin Brown Company
Charter Properties, Inc.
Peat Marwick Main & Co.
    F. Crowder Falls
    Robert G. Dinsmore, Jr.
    Jerry R. Licari
    Peter A. Mihaltian
WSOC Television, Inc. and
    WSOC Radio, Inc.
Mutual Savings & Loan Association of
    Charlotte, NC

Becon Construction Company, Inc.
Touchberry & Assoc. Inc., Realtors

CONTRIBUTORS

Adams Outdoor Advertising
Acuff Crane and Rigging
Alexander Julian, Inc.
Baucom Press
Belk Brothers Company
Carolina Motor Club
Charlotte Convention and Visitors Bureau
Charlotte/Mecklenburg Public Schools
The Charlotte Observer
Charlotte Transportation Authority
City of Charlotte
Creative Temporaries & Personnel
Duke Power Company
Dynair CSE Services, Inc.
Eva Gabor International
Gold Bond Building Products
EgyptAir
First Union National Bank
General Cinema
Guenoc Winery
Harris Teeter
Independence Center
Ivey's
Lawrence Transportation Systems,
    United Van Lines
Mercy Hospital
Mint Museum of Art Auxiliary
Myers Park High School
    Drama Department
North Carolina Air National Guard
North Carolina Division of Travel
    and Tourism
North Carolina State Legislature
Opera Carolina
Patterson Blake Incorporated
Pepsi-Cola Bottling Co. of
    Charlotte, Inc.
Piedmont Commuter, operated
    by CCAIR, Inc.
Piedmont Theatres
Prestige Wines
Princess Marcella Borghese
Queens College
Southern Bell
Shotwell & Partners Incorporated
Springs Industries, Inc.
Sunbelt Video
United States Postal Service
University of North Carolina, Charlotte
VUE Publishing Company
WBTV
Wells Fargo Armored Service
WSOC-TV

*A special note of thanks to the many contributors
of prizes and amenities for volunteers. We regret
any omission due to publication deadlines.*

Ramesses the Great Committees

RAMESSES STEERING COMMITTEE

Thomas Cox, Jr., *Chair*
Patty O'Herron Dewey
Karen M. Sachsenmaier

A. Zachary Smith, III
James W. Thompson

MARKETING ADVISORY COMMITTEE

John T. Fielder, *Chair*
Chapin A. Ferguson
Ervin Jackson, Jr.

Marc H. Silverman
Doug Stafford

GIFT SHOP ADVISORY COMMITTEE

Dave Stovall, *Chair*
Edward S. Dunn, Jr.
Roddy Kerr
John McCaskill

Al Rousso
Mrs. Paul J. Simon

OPENING EVENTS COMMITTEE

Patty O'Herron Dewey, *Chair*
Mrs. Thomas E. Cox, Jr.
Mrs. E. Reed Gaskin
Mrs. C. Scott McLanahan

Shay Merritt
Mrs. A. Zachary Smith, III
Mrs. James W. Thompson

VOLUNTEER ADVISORY COMMITTEE

Mrs. Dee Dee Murphy, *Chair*
Chris Bradburn
Brad Campbell
John Estes
Nancy Goode
Eric F. Grosse
Mrs. James R. Leavelle
Beth Maczka

Lisa Martinez
Joyce McSpadden
John Tabor
Mrs. William C. Taft
Nell H. Trombley
Betty VanderRoest

MINORITY INVOLVEMENT ADVISORY COMMITTEE

Mr. Harvey Gantt, *Honorary Chair*
Mrs. Dee Dee Murphy, *Chair*
Mrs. Jack S. Brayboy
Dr. Raleigh Bynum
Mrs. Wesley D. Clement
Ms. Willa Cline
Mrs. Howard Counts
Ms. Jackie Edwards
Mrs. James Ferguson
Mrs. Charles Farrar
Ms. Eleanor Graves
Mrs. Doris Guess
Ms. Betty Harris

Ms. Cathy Hughes
Rev. Clifford Jones
Mrs. Maurice McClettie
Ms. Alicia McCullough
Ms. Vivian Nivens
Mrs. Yvonne Stitt
Mrs. Gerson Stroud
Ms. Geraldine Sumpter
Mrs. A. J. Williams
Mrs. Vivian L. Williams

TEACHERS ADVISORY COMMITTEE

Jill R. Shuford, *Chair*
Ms. Deoborah Cooper
Mr. Ben Dupree
Mr. Dean Johns
Ms. Grace Mitchell

Carol Reid
Alice Rhodes
Mrs. Robert Shaw
Mr. Rob Williams

Mint Museum of Art
Board of Trustees

Staff

RAMESSES EXHIBITION STAFF AND SPECIAL CONSULTANTS

Milton J. Bloch, *Project Director*
Robert E. Bush, Jr., *Project Coordinator*

Charles L. Mo, *Curator*
Daniel Pincus Gottlieb, *Exhibition Designer*
Cheryl Palmer, *Educational Programs Coordinator*
Randy Wally, *Security and Maintenance Coordinator*
Stephen W. Musgrove, *Assistant Project Director*
Ann Thomasson, *Assistant Project Coordinator*
Phil Busher, *Public Relations Coordinator*
Arthur Bloomwell, *Ticket Sales Coordinator*
Janet Hart, *Volunteer Coordinator*
Pierrette Rouleau Stukes, *Special Events Coordinator*
Martha Tonissen Mayberry, *Transportation Coordinator*
Robert West, *Audio Visual Coordinator*
Margaret Callen, *Bookkeeper*
Kaky Cassada, *Assistant Ticket Sales Coordinator*
Susan Yoder, *Assistant Volunteer Coordinator*

David Silverman, *Consultant*
Katheryn Johnson, *Consultant*

Ramesses Gift Shop and Bazaar, Egyptian American Cultural Exchange, Inc., Ahmed Abdella, *President*

A special note of thanks to the entire Mint Museum of Art staff, whose collective contributions of time, effort and concern, helped make the exhibition successful.

MINT MUSEUM OF ART STAFF

Administration

Milton J. Bloch, *Executive Director*
Stephen W. Musgrove, *Deputy Director*
Delsie Maples, *Controller*
Millie Martin, *Assistant Controller*
Miriam Clark, *Administative Secretary*
Brenda Springs, *Office Assistant*
Angie Bayne, *Office Assistant*
Mary Ann Knighten, *Receptionist*

Curatorial

Charles L. Mo, *Curator of Art*
Anne Forcinito, *Assistant to the Curator of Art*
Mary Kilburn, *Assistant to the Curator*
Sheila K. Tabakoff, *Curator of Decorative Arts*
Vera Watts, *Assistant to the Curator of Decorative Arts*
Pat Roath, *Curator of Costumes*
Martha Tonissen Mayberry, *Registrar*
Libby Staub, *Assistant to the Registrar*

Design and Installation

Daniel Pincus Gottlieb, *Head of Design and Installation*
Kurt Warnke, *Chief Preparator*
Carol Ambrose, *Preparator*
Mitch Francis, *Carpenter*

Development

Robert E. Bush, Jr., *Director of Development*
Nancy H. Pingry, *Assistant Director of Development*
Phil Busher, *Public Relations Coordinator*
Pierrette Rouleau Stukes, *Special Events Coordinator*
Gerald L. Padbury, *Membership Assistant*

Education

Cheryl Palmer, *Director of Education*
Jill R. Shuford, *School Program Coordinator*
Robert West, *Audio Visual Coordinator*
Sara H. Wolf, *Librarian*

Security and Maintenance

Randy Wally, *Director of Building Services*
Robert McDowell, *Building Maintenance Supervisor*
Robert Sanders, *Security Shift Captain*
Annie Nesbitt, *Security Shift Lieutenant*
Doug Triplett, *Security Shift Lieutenant*
Arthur Allen, *Security Officer*
Dan Hamer, *Security Officer*
Gloria Harward, *Security Officer*
Celeste Herndon, *Security Officer*
Deborah Parham, *Security Officer*
Lisa Rick, *Security Officer*
Willie Anderson, *Maintenance Assistant*
Lovett Henderson, *Maintenance Assistant*
Leonard Howard, *Maintenance Assistant*
Vincell Staton, *Maintenance Assistant*

Acknowledgements

Ramesses the Great's empire succeeded and endured because of the participation and support of many. So, too, is this catalogue of his exploits and world the product of the ideas and assistance of Egyptologists and others from around the world. Its creation is the brainchild of the City of Memphis, especially Mayor Richard C. Hackett and Executive Director of the Exhibition and the City's Chief Administrative Officer, James E. Broughton. It has enjoyed the enthusiastic cooperation of the Egyptian Antiquities Organization, especially its former President, Dr. Gamal Mokhtar.

The catalogue attempts to recount the story of the life of Egypt's great King Ramesses II and his world to the interested lay public. Subjects discussed in the essay and their relative order reflect the nature and arrangement of the objects in the exhibition.

For sharing his expertise, I am especially grateful to Dr. Kenneth A. Kitchen of the University of Liverpool. The dates cited for events in the life of Ramesses the Great and his officials conform to Kitchen's chronology. For providing many new insights and for giving generously of their time to ensure the accuracy and completeness of this manuscript, I am indebted to James B. Manning of New York and Memphis State University, Richard Fazzini of The Brooklyn Museum, Bernard V. Bothmer of the Institute of Fine Arts of New York University, and Peter Shapiro of New York. Additionally, I wish to thank my colleagues Janine Bourriau, Susan K. Doll, Zahi Hawass, Cathleen Keller and John McIntire.

For not only granting me access to their photographic archives and research libraries but also for making me feel at home therein, I am grateful additionally to the following institutions and individuals: Center of Documentation and Studies on Ancient Egypt (C.E.D.A.E.), especially Dr. Abdel-Aziz Sadek; the Department of Egyptian, Classical and Ancient Middle Eastern Art and Wilbour Library of The Brooklyn Museum, especially, Dr. Robert S. Bianchi, James F. Romano, Dr. Ogden Goelet, Vicki Solia, and Diane Guzman; the Department of Egyptian and Ancient Near Eastern Art of the Museum of Fine Arts, Boston, especially Dr. Edward Brovarski, Peter Lacovara, Sue D'Auria, Catharine A. Roehrig, Dr. Timothy Kendall and Peter der Manuelian; the Department of Egyptian Art of the Metropolitan Museum of Art, especially Dr. Christine Lilyquist and Marsha Hill; the National Geographic Society, especially Dori Babyak; and Barbara Shattuck, and the Manning/Pleskow Archive in New York.

The majority of the excellent photographs of Ramesside monuments included here are the work of Jon Abbott, who, with his assistant Anne Edgerton, accompanied me in the footsteps of Ramesses II from Qantir to Abu Simbel during the dog days of July. For their courage and persistance, I am especially grateful. Credit for the ease with which our work was accomplished belongs to the Egyptian Antiquities Organization, especially Dr. Gamal Mokhtar, Dr. Ahmed Kadry, Dr. Mohamed Saleh, Galal Sharawy, Abdin Siam and Rada ali Soliman.

Also present with me in Egypt was world-renowned photographer William Eggleston, on assignment for Memphis Brooks Museum of Art. He and Memphis Brooks have generously allowed a selection of his work to be included here as an introductory photographic essay.

For their kindness in supplying previously unpublished excavation material, I am grateful to the following expeditions: the Egypt Exploration Society Memphis Project, especially Professor H.S. Smith and David Jeffreys; the joint Egypt Exploration Society-Rijksmuseum van Oudheden, Leiden Expedition to the New Kingdom Necropolis at Saqqara, especially Geoffrey T. Martin; the Qantir Expedition of the Pelizaeus-Museum, Hildesheim, especially Dr. Edgar Pusch; The Brooklyn Museum Mut Expedition, especially Richard Fazzini and Mary McKercher; and the Wadi Tumilat Project of the University of Toronto, especially Phyllis and John S. Holladay, Jr.

To all those involved in its production, this catalogue was more than just a job. For their personal concern, and hard work, special thanks are due technical planning coordinator Glen Campbell, catalogue project coordinator Nancy E. Bogatin, editor Liz Conway, consulting editor Carol Lynn Yellin, index compiler Catherine C. Swearingen, and contributing editor Valerie Moore.

Dedicated assistant Lynn Gipson and IEAA Curator of Education Anna Kay Walker helped in a myriad way at all hours, often at a moment's notice. In this regard, I wish also to thank Emily Sharp, Edward Orio, Diane Reed, Jane Jarvi, Elizabeth Powell, James R. Wagner and Lucia Burch, as well as typists Kipp Williams, Brenda Landman, Betty Leigh Hutcheson and Nancy Douglass.

The richness of color reproduction and attractive appearance of the catalogue is due in large measure to the uncompromising standards and generosity of Lithograph Printing Company, especially Vice President Herbert "Dutch" Akers, Mike Hines and Sheila Hudson, as well as Ronnie Stoots and the staff of Marcol Graphics.

For granting me time to work on the catalogue, and, as always, for their support and encouragement, I thank Dr. Richard R. Ranta, Dean of the College of Communication and Fine Arts of Memphis State University, Dr. Carol J. Crown, Chairman of its Department of Art, and my colleague at the Institute of Egyptian Art and Archaeology, Dr. Edward Bleiberg.

To all these individuals and institutions, a sincere "thank you" for helping to make this catalogue all we wanted it to be.

R.E.F.

Egyptian Chronology

PREDYNASTIC PERIOD
(4000-3200 B.C.)
*Communal settlements.
Domestication of animals and
plants. Decorated pottery, flint
tools, slate palettes, jewelry buried
with dead in individual graves
in cemeteries.*

 Badarian
 Amratian (Nagada I)
 Gerzean (Nagada II)

EARLY DYNASTIC I-II
(3200-2780 B.C.)
*Unification of Upper and Lower
Egypt. Formative period for
architecture, art, language.*

Dynasty I: 3200-2980 B.C.
Dynasty II: 2980-2780 B.C.

OLD KINGDOM III-VI
(2780-2258 B.C.)
*Pyramid Age. King as
manifestation of god on earth and
absolute authority. Rise of sun cult.
Memphis as center of politics, art,
learning. Classical age for art.*

Dynasty III: 2780-2680 B.C.
Dynasty IV: 2680-2565 B.C.
Dynasty V: 2565-2420 B.C.
Dynasty VI: 2420-2258 B.C.

**FIRST INTERMEDIATE
PERIOD VII-X**
(2258-2052 B.C.)
*Dissolution of central monarchy.
Usurpation of power by provincial
leaders. Decline in art styles.*

Dynasty VII: Interregnum
Dynasty VIII (Memphite):
 2258-2232 B.C.
Dynasty IX (Heracleopolitan):
 2232-2140 B.C.
Dynasty X (Heracleopolitan):
 2140-2052 B.C.

MIDDLE KINGDOM XI-XII
(2134-1786 B.C.)
*Reunification of Egypt and
reestablishment of central
monarchy. King as careworn good
shepherd. Rise of cult of Osiris.
Democratization of religious
beliefs. Classical age for language.*

Dynasty XI: 2134-1991 B.C.
Dynasty XII: 1991-1786 B.C.

**SECOND INTERMEDIATE
PERIOD XIII-XVII**
(1786-1570 B.C.)
*Again dissolution of central
monarchy. Hyksos invade from the
east.*

Dynasties XIII-XIV: 1786-1680 B.C.
 about thirty kings partly
 contemporaneous
Dynasties XV-XVI: 1720-1570 B.C.
 Hyksos in north; local rulers in
 Thebes
Dynasty XVII: 1600-1570 B.C.

NEW KINGDOM XVIII-XX
(1570-1085 B.C.)
*Expulsion of Hyksos and
conquest of empire to south and
east. Amun as national god.
Theban temples amass vast wealth.
Akhenaten and wife Nefertiti
renounce cult of Amun and
establish the sun disk as sole
god. Capital moves to Amarna.
Naturalism in art. Tutankhamun
restores old religion and moves
back to Thebes.*

Dynasty XVIII: 1570-1314 B.C.
 Ahmose I
 Amunhotep I
 Tuthmosis I
 Tuthmosis II
 Hatshepsut
 Tuthmosis III
 Amunhotep II
 Tuthmosis IV
 Amunhotep III
 Akhenaten
 Semenkhkare
 Tut-ankh-amun
 Ay
 Horemheb
Dynasty XIX: 1314-1197 B.C.
 Ramesses I
 Sety I
 Ramesses II
 Merneptah
 Amunmesse
 Sety II
 Siptah (Merneptah)
 Tausert
Dynasty XX: 1197-1085 B.C.
 Seth-nakht
 Ramesses III
 Ramesses IV-Ramesses XI

**THIRD INTERMEDIATE
PERIOD XXI-XXIV**
(1085-715 B.C.)
*Authority divided between
powerful priesthood at Thebes
and ruling family in Delta.*

Dynasty XXI (Tanis and Thebes):
 1085-950 B.C.

Dynasty XXII (Bubastite):
 950-730 B.C.
Dynasty XXIII: 817 (?)-730 B.C.
 Six kings contemporaneous with
 the end of Dynasty XXII
Dynasty XXIV: 730-715 B.C.

LATE PERIOD XXV-XXXI
(730-332 B.C.)
*Alternation between foreign and
native rulers. Artistic revival.
Development of true portraiture.*

Dynasty XXV (Kushite):
 730-656 B.C.
Assyrian invasion:
 Esarhaddon captures Memphis:
 671 B.C.
 Ashurbanipal sacks Thebes:
 663 B.C.
Dynasty XXVI (Saite): 664-525 B.C.
Persian invasion under Cambyses:
 525 B.C.
Dynasty XXVII: First Persian
 Domination:
 525-404 B.C.
Dynasties XXVIII-XXIX:
 404-378 B.C.
 Six kings maintain independence
 against Persia
Dynasty XXX: 378-341 B.C.
Dynasty XXXI: Second Persian
 Domination: 341-332 B.C.
Conquest of Alexander: 332 B.C.

MACEDONIAN KINGS
(331-304 B.C.)
Conquest by Alexander the Great

PTOLEMAIC DYNASTY
(304-30 B.C.)
*Establishment of Greek ruling
family. Extensive temple building.
Mixture of Greek and Egyptian
styles.*

ROMAN PERIOD
(30 B.C.-A.D. 640)
*Conquest by Augustus Caesar.
Exploitation for Roman Empire.
Egyptian cults forbidden by edict
of Constantine. Conversion to
Christianity.*

ISLAMIC PERIOD
(A.D. 640 to present)
*Conquest by Muslims and
conversion to Islam.*

Adapted from W.S. Smith, *The Art
and Architecture of Ancient Egypt*,
revised with additions by W.K.
Simpson (Middlesex, England:
Penguin, 1981).

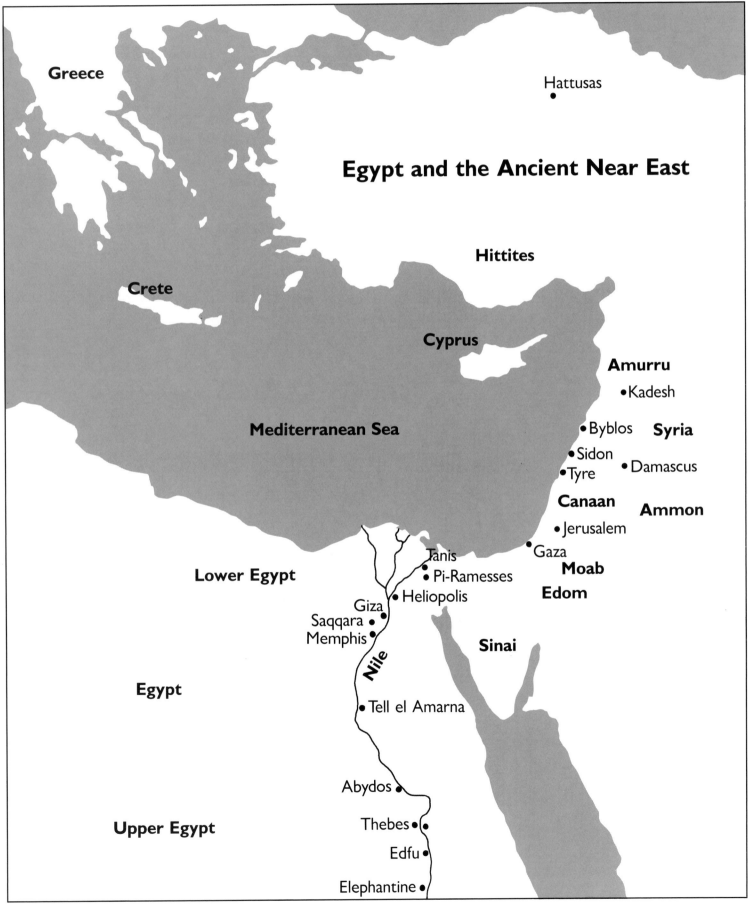

Egypt and the Ancient Near East

Greece

Hattusas

Hittites

Crete

Cyprus

Amurru

•Kadesh

Mediterranean Sea

•Byblos   Syria

•Sidon   •Damascus

•Tyre

Canaan   Ammon

•Jerusalem

Lower Egypt

Tanis   Gaza

•Pi-Ramesses   Moab

•Heliopolis   Edom

Giza

Saqqara   Sinai

Memphis

Nile

Egypt

•Tell el Amarna

Abydos

Upper Egypt

Thebes•

Edfu

Elephantine•

Mediterranean Sea

Kom el Hisn •
Avaris • Tanis
Bubastis • **Pi-Ramesses**
Kom abu Billo • • Tell el Maskhuta
• Tell el Yahudiya
Lower Egypt • Heliopolis
Giza •
Saqqara •
Memphis •
Fayum
• Lahun
Gurob •

Sinai

Serabit el Khadem •

Upper Egypt

Ashmunein •
• Tell el Amarna

Assiut •

• Akhmim

Red Sea

Abydos • Dendera
Quft • - - - **Wadi Hammamat**
Armant • • **Thebes**
• Tod
Kharga Oasis Esna •
• Elkab
Edfu •
• Gebel Silsileh
• Kom Ombo
Elephantine • **First Cataract**

Beit el Wali •
Lower Nubia Gerf Hussein •
• Quban
Wadi Sebua •
• Derr
Abu Simbel •
Buhen •
Second Cataract
Semna • **Upper Nubia**

• Amara
Egypt and Nubia
Soleb •
Sesebi •

The Colossus of Memphis

Skillfully carved in granite from Aswan, the 24 foot, seven inch tall colossus journeyed 600 miles down river to Memphis, the glorious capital of ancient Egypt. Almighty Ramesses, pharaoh with dominion over Egypt's empire, would live forever in stone.

Ramesses the Great, identified by name on both the belt of his pleated royal kilt and on the statue's base, appears as he wished the world to remember him. He strides forward regally, left foot first in the traditional pose of Egyptian male figures. His arms hang at his sides, and in his right fist he clasps a folded bolt of cloth. The white crown of Upper Egypt (Nile Valley) rests on his head, and a long straight beard anchored to his chin with a strap further proclaims his royal status. Jewels adorn his strong neck and powerful wrists, and a daggar hangs from his belt. Ramesses' figure is youthfully trim, and his noble countenance was rendered with particular care.

Ramesses dedicated this colossus to Ptah, the patron god of Memphis. It flanked one of the small temples along the processional way leading to the main south gate of the sacred enclosure of the temple of Ptah. Perhaps, it stood beside a companion statue of similar scale wearing the Lower Egyptian (Delta) crown.

Other kings before and after erected colossal statues of themselves, but none are larger in size or greater in number than the ones commissioned by Ramesses the Great. Throughout Egypt and Nubia, these colossi stood like guardians beside temple facades or inside open temple courts. By their magnitude and their presence on sacred temple grounds, the statues provided tangible and awe inspiring reminders of the earthly power of Ramesses the Great and of his closeness to the gods. These statues embodied both the essence of kingship and divinity. They functioned as intermediaries between the people of Egypt and the inaccessible gods inside the

Conservators moved the Colossus of Memphis in preparation for restoration.

Restoration of the Colossus of Memphis was conducted on site, only yards away from where the statue had been buried for centuries!

Ramsy Nageeb served as architect on the project. Abd Allah el Hossany and Hamdiny held the positions of chief restorers.

temples. Passers-by delivering petitions and prayers relied on Ramesses the Great to intercede with the gods on their humble behalf.

Ramesses the Great erected at least ten other larger than life statues of himself in the vicinity of the temple of Ptah. Although only fragments of most remain, two others have survived the centuries and are among Egypt's finest and most famous monuments. One stands in front of Cairo's bustling railroad station at an intersection known as Ramesses Square. The other lies in its own open-air museum near where it once stood in ancient Memphis.

At an unknown time in history and by perpetrators unidentified, a heavy blunt instrument reduced the great Colossus of Memphis to ruin. This once splendid statue fell on its left side and wind-blown earth covered it.

For centuries, Ramesses' colossus was lost to the world. In 1962 it was rediscovered behind the present open-air museum by machinery digging the foundation for a restaurant. Construction immediately stopped, and the statue's three largest pieces were moved onto wood pilings to prevent further ravages by the elements. Thus, through the colossus, Ramesses regained his place as a commanding presence in ancient Memphis.

In early 1986, after visiting Memphis, Egypt, delegations led by Mayor Richard C. Hackett of Memphis, Tennessee, recognized the beauty and significance of these magnificent ruins and requested that the Egyptian Antiquities Organization include the Colossus of Memphis in the Memphis showing of the *Ramesses the Great* exhibition. Egyptian officials agreed, and consultations with international art experts commenced. Coca-Cola USA generously offered to fund the project, and restoration began on the statue in Memphis, Egypt, during June of 1986. When the Denver Museum of Natural History learned of Memphis' efforts, they offered to participate in the restoration project.

Approximately 30 conservators worked 16 hours daily through January 1987 to reassemble the three large pieces and many smaller fragments. Steel pins were added for stability and strength. Artisans reconstructed the missing knee area of the right leg, right foot and parts of the base, using powdered granite, poured concrete and steel rods. A back slab, added for increased support, replaced a smaller back pillar. The restored colossus now weighs 57 tons.

In preparation for its journey to Memphis on the Mississippi, Lloyd's of London insured the precious treasure. Conservators disassembled the statue into three pieces and packed it into wooden crates (adding yet another four tons!). An Egyptian army honor guard escorted the heavy transport trucks which took the colossus from Memphis, Egypt to Mediterranean shores at Alexandria. There, under the close supervision of Antiquities Organization officials, the wooden crates were packed in a steel case and placed aboard the *Aquila*. A military band and a naval escort into international waters provided a befitting royal send-off as the colossus departed for the port of Marseilles, France on February 5, 1987. The colossus' incredible journey continued as it was transferred to the *Express* for its Atlantic crossing bound for Savannah, Georgia. It arrived on U.S. shores in late February, and early in March, two huge trucks caravaned to the Memphis Convention Center.

To accommodate the colossus of Ramesses the Great, tiles had to be removed from the Memphis Convention Center's 38 foot ceiling. A 45 ton forklift and 50 ton crane, supplied by Acuff Crane and Rigging Company, reassembled the statue on a steel girded weight distribution platform.

The statue which once stood as temple guardian and petitioner of the gods now stands as the focal point of the *Ramesses the Great* exhibition in Charlotte where it bridges thousands of years and thousands of miles. The statue of the great petitioner was petitioned for, and restored by, a remarkable cooperative effort led by Mayor Richard C. Hackett, the City of Memphis, Tennessee, the Egyptian Antiquities Organization, the Denver Museum of Natural History and the generosity of Coca-Cola USA.

The colossus inspired awe then, and it inspires awe now. Ramesses has seen Memphis in ancient Egypt and Memphis in the 20th century United States. Today, it serves as a symbol of cooperation between two great countries, and it will continue to stand as a timeless testimony to the power of international friendship.

With restoration almost completed, the Colossus of Memphis once again assumes its proper position.

Ramesses the Great's Colossus: from Ancient Memphis to Modern Memphis

1279-1213 B.C.	Ramesses the Great commissions a larger than life statue of himself to stand outside the Ptah Temple precinct at Memphis.
B.C.-A.D.	Ancient despoilers destroy the statue with heavy blunt instruments. Lying broken on its side, desert winds shift earth which eventually covers the colossus.
A.D. 1962	Egyptian construction workers unexpectedly make an important archaeological discovery! They find statue fragments while digging a foundation for a new restaurant.
1962-1984	Lack of funds precludes restoration of this once magnificent treasure.
December, 1984	Memphis, Tennessee, Mayor Richard C. Hackett leads a delegation to ancient Memphis and expresses interest in bringing the statue to Memphis, Tennessee.
February, 1985	*Ramesses the Great* exhibition officials visit Egypt and formally request permission from the Egyptian Antiquities Organization to include Ramesses' colossus in the Memphis exhibition.
	Egyptian Antiquities Organization informs Memphis that the statue must be restored before leaving its Egyptian homeland.
	Egyptian officials sign a letter of intent to include the statue as part of the Canadian and U.S. tour of the *Ramesses the Great* exhibition.
August, 1985	Egyptian officials sign *Ramesses the Great* exhibition contract minus provisions for the Colossus of Memphis. All parties understand that separate agreements must be reached to include the colossus.
January, 1986	James H. Franz of the Metropolitan Museum of Art, New York and Michael S. Fletcher, an engineer with the architectural firm Skidmore, Owings & Merrill, journey to Egypt and prepare feasibility study on the statue's restoration. The Memphis *Commercial Appeal* funds their study.
March/April, 1986	*Ramesses the Great* exhibition officials verbally agree to underwrite the Egyptian Antiquities Organization's $100,000 cost of restoring the Colossus of Memphis.
June, 1986	Although written agreement is not signed, restoration begins.

	Mediterranean en route to Alexandria. New travel provisions are quickly arranged.
February, 1987	Colossus crates are placed in heavy steel container for protection on board the *M.V. Aquila*. Full military honors accompany the statue as it leaves the Alexandria harbor.
February, 1987	The colossus of Ramesses the Great arrives in Marseilles, France. Its crates are transferred to the *Express* for the arduous Atlantic crossing.
February, 1987	The *Express* sails for Savannah, Georgia with its priceless cargo.
February, 1987	The Colossus of Memphis reaches American soil and is transferred to two trucks.
March, 1987	The colossus completes its journey from ancient Memphis to modern Memphis, Tennessee! Memphis' Acuff Crane and Rigging provides 45 ton forklift and 50 ton crane to install the Colossus of Memphis at the Memphis Convention Center.
April 15, 1987	*Ramesses the Great* exhibition opens in Memphis, Tennessee with the modern world premier showing of the Colossus of Memphis.
September, 1987	The Colossus of Memphis departs modern Memphis for exhibition at the Denver Museum of Natural History.
April, 1988	The Colossus of Memphis departs Denver for exhibition at the Boston Museum of Science.
September, 1988	The Colossus of Memphis departs Boston for exhibition at the Mint Museum, Charlotte, N.C.
Post 1988	The Colossus of Memphis will permanently reside in the courtyard of the Museum of Civilization in Cairo as a testimony to international friendship.

Eggleston's Egypt

The following nine pages contain works drawn from the *Egyptian Project Portfolio* by internationally known color photographer William Eggleston. During the summer of 1986, Eggleston journeyed to the lands of Ramesses the Great in an effort to capture a distinctive and fresh view of Egypt. These photographs accurately reflect in microcosm what resulted in Eggleston's *Egyptian Project.*

Memphis Brooks Museum of Art initiated and sponsored Eggleston's project which had no creative restraints or limitations in its commission. Consequently, he was afforded the rare luxury of approaching his assignment in the tradition of nineteenth century photographic expeditions. Before retracing the footsteps of Ramesses the Great, Eggleston joined Dr. Rita E. Freed in Cairo for an orientation to the land of the pharaohs. For three weeks, Eggleston surveyed Egypt's virtually limitless field of images with his vintage Leica camera. The photographs selected convey a sense of order and composition unique to Eggleston while they also accurately reflect what it is like to be in Egypt. Consequently, the images offer many layers of meaning to both casual viewers and to sophisticated students of fine photography.

Eggleston's Egypt in Microcosm

Horizontal Head of Ramesses II, Mid 13th c. B.C., Memphis, Egypt, *pages 12-13.*

Ram-Headed Sphinxes, Processional Avenue, Temple of Amun-Re, Karnak, *pages 14-15.*

Granite Torso of Merneptah in two pieces, *page 16.*

Ruins With Palm Trees Near Memphis, *page 17.*

Mortuary Temple of Queen Hatshepsut, Deir El-Bahari, ca. 1450 b.c., *pages 18-19.*

Square Stacked Rocks Sporting Rebil of Ptah, Palm Trees Above, *page 20.*

I
Ramesses the King

The Nile at Gebel Silsileh.

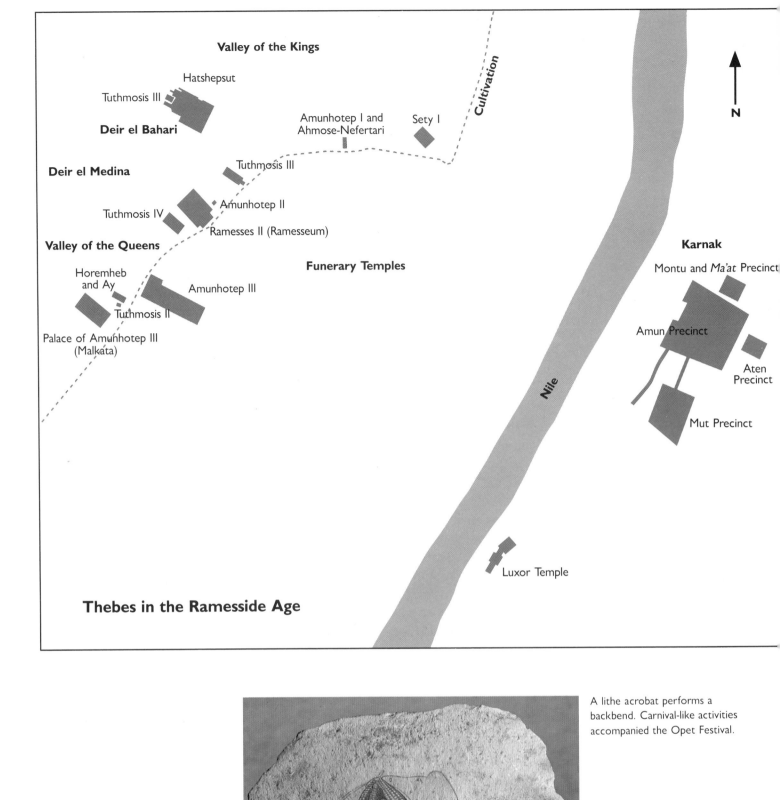

Thebes in the Ramesside Age

Valley of the Kings

Hatshepsut

Tuthmosis III

Deir el Bahari

Amunhotep I and
Ahmose-Nefertari

Sety I

Cultivation

N

Tuthmosis III

Deir el Medina

Tuthmosis IV

Amunhotep II

Ramesses II (Ramesseum)

Valley of the Queens

Funerary Temples

Horemheb
and Ay

Amunhotep III

Tuthmosis II

Palace of Amunhotep III
(Malkata)

Nile

Karnak

Montu and *Ma'at* Precinct

Amun Precinct

Aten
Precinct

Mut Precinct

Luxor Temple

Ramess
warrior
scepter

A lithe acrobat performs a
backbend. Carnival-like activities
accompanied the Opet Festival.

and souvenir hawkers provided entertainment for all. At the end, when Amun returned to his home at Karnak, Ramesses II left Thebes secure in his new role as divine king. After his visit, the king demonstrated his gratitude by adding a court-yard, a pylon (monumental gateway), colossal statues and obelisks to the Luxor temple.

Returning downstream, Ramesses II stopped at Abydos, a holy city and traditional burial place of Osiris, the god of resurrection. Ramesses later described in a dedicatory inscription what greeted him there: "He found the temples of the necropolis which belonged to former kings...fallen into a state of disrepair...no two bricks were together...No son was there who would refurbish the monument of his father."[1]

One of a number of colossal statues of King Ramesses II flanking the columns of the first court of the Luxor temple.

Instilled from an early age with a reverence for his ancestors, Ramesses II corrected the sad situation in Abydos by completing their temples, restoring their tombs and establishing their endowment in perpetuity. In a smart political move aimed at placing the priesthood firmly in his camp and under his control, he promoted a local Abydene priest, Nebwenenef, to the office of high priest of Amun at Thebes, the most powerful priestly position in the land.

Leaving Abydos, Ramesses continued north into Lower Egypt to the Eastern Delta, near Avaris, probably the native city of his ancestors, where his father had erected a summer palace. It was in this area, close to the Waters of Ra (Pelusiac branch of the Nile), that Ramesses II decided to establish a new capital city. He named his city Pi-Ramesses (the House of Ramesses, beloved of Amun, Great of Victories), and he erected a heaven on earth.

Contemporary accounts hint at the magnificence of Pi-Ramesses. The king's palace, large and lavishly decorated, occupied a central location in the city. Its great limestone columns and its massive mudbrick walls, overlaid with a casing of glazed faience tiles, must have loomed high above the flatness of the Delta terrain. Doorways, window frames, balconies and the platform of the king's throne featured faience tile decorations showing foreign captives, vassals paying tribute and lions devouring prisoners, all calculated to awe the onlooker. The harem's decorative tiles, in contrast, featured lighthearted themes, such as floral designs (Cat. No. 34), aquatic life (Cat. Nos. 30-32) and carefree maidens (Cat. No. 33). These tiles, too, were made

Pi-Ramesses in the Ramesside Age

Little remains of Ramesses II's Delta capital Pi-Ramesses, now under excavation by the Pelizaeus Museum, Hildesheim, West Germany.

One of at least 24 lofty obelisks erected by Ramesses the Great at Pi-Ramesses. Now they lie in ruin at Tanis.

Piece by piece, the temples, statues and obelisks of Pi-Ramesses were moved to the new capital at Tanis by the kings of Dynasty XXI.

from faience, a ceramic covered with glaze, and their color dazzled the eye. An official writing during the reign of Ramesses II's son, Merneptah, would liken the material to turquoise and lapis lazuli.

A large lake, living quarters for princes, priests and high-echelon bureaucrats, a military training ground and barracks, and a zoo occupied the area around the palace. (Lion, gazelle, giraffe and elephant bones aided archaeologists in identifying the site of the zoo.) Archives, administrative buildings, workshops, open-air markets, a harbor, warehouses and granaries, separated from each other by lakes and canals, also contributed to the bustling atmosphere of Pi-Ramesses.

The city continued to flourish after Ramesses II's reign, but slowly, over the next 200 years, the river branch which flowed to its west silted up and changed course northward. Pi-Ramesses was cut off, and the rulers of Dynasty XXI established a new capital city at Tanis. Rather than transport vast amounts of newly cut stone from distant quarries, they simply dismantled the monuments of Ramesses II's old capital and used the stone to build their own temples. Today, so little remains *in situ* from Ramesses II's grand Delta city that the average visitor to the original site, in the area of modern Qantir, would hardly be aware that an important ancient metropolis had ever existed there.

Ramesses II sponsored active building programs in other cities, especially Memphis, Egypt's first capital and her strongest link to the ancient past. We know less about Memphis than many other ancient capital cities because so much has been removed, destroyed by a rising water table or still lies buried. We do know, however, that the city grew and prospered under Ramesses II's rule. Of the extant monuments, the majority bear the cartouche of Ramesses the Great.

Memphis in the Ramesside Age was a political, military and religious hub. Central to the city, most likely, was the large temple precinct (ca. 3774 x 2625 feet) of Memphis' patron god, Ptah. Ramesses II may have been crowned here. According to a myth promoted by the Memphis priesthood, Ptah, in his role as creator of the universe, was the god of craftsmen, and workshops of many artisans were located outside his temple. Ramesses II's palace probably lay near the sacred area, but to date none of its remains have been identified.

With its location at the southern tip of the Delta, Memphis had truly been a "river city" from at least the time of the Old Kingdom. It guarded the entrance to the Nile Valley, and its harbor served as a departure point for ships destined for Mediterranean ports. (Because of silting, the river changed course, and the precise location of the Ramesside port awaits discovery.) Memphis was a vast ship-building center where seagoing vessels and boats of all sizes which traveled the Nile were constructed and repaired. The industry required timber yards, carpenters' workshops and toolmakers' quarters. Some of the ships produced in Memphis dockyards joined Pharaoh's fleet. The city's importance as a center of commerce and communication made it a strategic military area. Troops were garrisoned there, and infantry and chariotry conducted maneuvers and fought mock battles within the city's boundaries. Arsenals warehoused chariots and weapons which had been manufactured in Memphis workshops.

All the personnel required to staff and administer the military installations, workshops, palace, temples and port, as well as the auxiliary industries which grew up around them, made Memphis a key residential center, probably Egypt's largest.

The Ptah temple precinct at Memphis.

**Memphis in the Ramesside Age
Ptah Temple Precinct**

Temple of Ptah

N

hypostyle hall

small Ptah temple

sphinx

wayside chapel

Processional Way

Hathor temple

Houses and workshops of Ramesside artisans lie at the southwest corner of the Ptah temple precinct at Memphis. They were recently excavated by the Egypt Exploration Society.

A temple to Hathor in ancient Memphis.

After a dreadful beating, enemy spies revealed the whereabouts of the Hittite troops. From Abu Simbel.

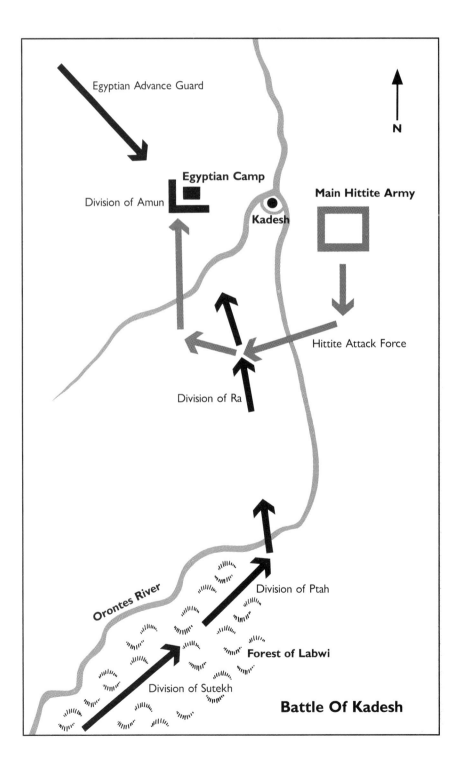

Egyptian Advance Guard

N

Egyptian Camp

Division of Amun

Kadesh

Main Hittite Army

Hittite Attack Force

Division of Ra

Division of Ptah

Orontes River

Forest of Labwi

Division of Sutekh

Battle Of Kadesh

A place of beauty and cultural vitality, Memphis enjoyed the devotion of her citizens. One homesick Memphite living at the end of Dynasty XIX wrote of how his heart "hastens to a place that it knows...Come to me, O Ptah, that you may take me to Memphis." [2] Another wrote, "The like of Memphis has never been seen." [3]

Warrior and Peacemaker

Rumors of trouble in the Levant in Year 4 forced Ramesses II to put aside his concentration upon the ongoing massive construction projects and focus his attention on less peaceful concerns. The relative stability of Egypt's vassal states along the eastern Mediterranean coast and her control of other vital trade routes of the Ancient Near East had been weakened since late in Dynasty XVIII by the growing strength of the Hittite empire in Anatolia (modern Turkey). As Prince-Regent, Ramesses II had accompanied his father on a campaign to the Levant to re-establish control of the coastal area and mastery over the city of Kadesh, an important crossroad in northern Amurru, an area that included Syria and Lebanon. Kadesh, straddling the northern tip of Lebanon's mountain ranges and controlling passage south into the Bekaa Valley and east from there through the Eleutheros Valley to the sea, had again fallen under Hittite control. Ramesses II was determined to recapture the prize.

In April of Year 5, Ramesses the Great left Egypt with an army of about 20,000 men, one of the largest military forces the Near East had ever seen. Four divisions of about 5,000 men each made the long march north along the coast of Canaan, then inland to the Bekaa Valley. Meanwhile, Pharaoh's advance guard, a small force of the king's elite, moved forward along a different route. Each division included infantry and chariotry; each traveled under the divine protection and standard of one of Egypt's main gods and under the command of Ramesses II or one of his sons. The entire force, with its chariots, herald trumpeters, supply wagons and camp followers, must have stretched for miles. This army, traveling an estimated two miles per hour, might have covered 15 miles on a good day.

Within a month the Egyptian forces reached the Orontes River, less than ten miles from Kadesh. A pair of captured spies lied, asserting that the enemy forces were still some 120 miles to the north near Aleppo. Therefore, Ramesses II's Amun division, followed closely by the Ra Division, crossed the Orontes and continued toward Kadesh, establishing camp just west of the city. Then Egyptian scouts seized two more spies who, after a hearty flogging, begged for mercy and revealed that the Hittite

King Ramesses II repulses the Hittites. From Luxor.

army was actually only minutes away on the other side of Kadesh! Upon hearing this dreadful news, Ramesses II immediately dispatched mounted messengers to summon his troops, half of which had yet to ford the Orontes. Moments later, the Hittites attacked.

Under the Hittite banner, King Muwatallis had amassed an army even larger than Egypt's. Hired mercenaries and pirates from a vast area had joined native Hittites to make up two groups of fighting men about 18,000 and 19,000 strong. In addition, there were 2,500 chariots. The Hittite chariotry now smashed into the division of Ra which was behind that of Amun. In frenzied flight from charging chariots, the soldiers of Ra burst into Ramesses II's encamped Amun Division, which also scattered in panic.

Finding himself abandoned by all but his personal guard and his shield-bearer, Ramesses II prayed to the god Amun: "I call upon thee, my father Amun, for I am in the midst of a multitude of foes."[4] And Amun gave him strength. Virtually alone, Ramesses II charged the enemy in his chariot. "All about him was the heat of fire,"[5] according to one inscription. "He was mighty, his heart stout."[6]

Fortunately, just at that moment, Ramesses II's elite advance guard, which had been traveling a separate route to Kadesh, appeared and entered the battle. Attacked now from two flanks, the Hittites hastily retreated. King Muwatallis sent auxiliaries, but to no avail. A third Egyptian force, the division of Ptah, had arrived and joined the melee. When Ramesses II set up camp that night on the battlefield, even the cowardly warriors from Amun and Ra came drifting back. The next day Ramesses led them in a fresh onslaught. The battle ended in a stalemate.

For the Hittites, it had been a near disaster. With the bulk of his chariotry captured, a brother killed and many of his chief officers wounded, King Muwatallis begged for peace.

It must have been a joyous moment in camp, as the Egyptian forces surveyed their booty of chariots, horses, armor, bows, arrows, swords, daggers, shields and prisoners. To calculate enemy casualties, Egyptian soldiers lopped off the hands of the dead Hittite soldiers, tossing them in a pile as scribes recorded their numbers.

Ramesses II led his troops home in triumph and proclaimed to the four corners of the earth how his heroism in the face of adversity had saved the day. The story of the Battle of Kadesh is related in prose, poetry and illustration on temples he built throughout the land. It can be seen today at Abydos, Karnak, twice at the Ramesseum (his funerary temple near the Valley of the Kings) and three times at Luxor. In Nubia it may be seen at Abu Simbel, and it once existed at Derr as well. Each time Ramesses II told the story, it became a bit more elaborate, but in every case he

Egyptian chariots (left) proved superior to those of the Hittites (right) at the battle of Kadesh. Note the different shields. From Abu Simbel.

Ramesses II slays foreign enemies.
From Memphis.

neglected to point out that, despite his valor, the battle had changed nothing. The Hittites, after all, retained possession of Kadesh.

For a full 15 years following the Battle of Kadesh, skirmishes and constantly shifting alliances continued to plague the Egyptian empire at its borders. Those years saw Ramesses II back on the battlefield in Canaan, Lebanon and Syria, as petty kingdoms resisted Egyptian supremacy and neglected to send tribute.

and his daughters, Meryetamun (Cat. No. 2), Bint-Anath and Nebettawy, also recei
the title Great Royal Wife.

A Hittite princess, King Hattusil III's daughter to whom the Egyptians gave
the name Maathorneferure, became one of Ramesses II's chief wives in Year 34.
Diplomatic "state" marriages were not uncommon in Ancient Near Eastern society
for both sides profited. To renew their bonds of friendship and to reconfirm their
peace treaty of Year 21, King Hattusil III, some 13 years later, offered his oldest
daughter to Ramesses II in marriage (or so states the Egyptian account). Her lavish
dowry undoubtedly made this offer especially attractive to Ramesses II.

In late fall of 1246 B.C., the Hittite princess left her homeland accompanied by

Of his many wives, Nefertari was
Ramesses II's favorite, based upon
the many monuments he built in her
honor. Her tomb at Thebes contains
some of the finest painting of the
Ramesside era.

ambassadors, dignitaries and soldiers who guarded not only this retinue but also, according to one of the commemorative stelae later erected, "a very great tribute...of gold, silver, copper in great quantities, slaves, horses without limit, cattle, goats and sheep by the ten-thousands." [7] Ramesses II sent his delegation to meet the Hittites and regally escort them to Egypt. On a delightfully balmy February day in 1245 B.C. (weather arranged courtesy of Pharaoh through a special prayer to Sutekh in his role as god of the weather), the party arrived at the gates at Pi-Ramesses. There Ramesses II gazed for the first time upon his bride, and, we are told, "She was beautiful in the heart of his majesty, and he loved her more than anything." [8]

So proud was he of his new bride that he proclaimed her arrival throughout the land. The text of the "Marriage Stela" has been found at Karnak, on the isle of Elephantine at Aswan, and further south in Nubia at Aksha, Abu Simbel and Amara West. In later state marriages, Ramesses II took another Hittite princess, a Babylonian princess and a Syrian princess into his harem.

Exactly how many children Ramesses II's great royal wives and his lesser wives bore, we do not know, but recent assessments place the number at around 90 (approximately 50 boys and 40 girls). Sons and daughters appear with the king in birth-order procession on temple walls and beside him on statuary. Sons accompanied him in battle. Like his father before him, Ramesses II trained them in the art of kingship.

As adults, some of Ramesses the Great's children aided him in administering the country and promoting his ideals. His fourth son, Khaemwase, inherited his father's interest in Egypt's splendid past and became the country's first archaeologist. He was later revered by Greek and Roman conquerors of Egypt as a scholar and a magician. Appointed to the priesthood at Memphis as a youth and eventually assuming the office of high priest, Khaemwase studied the ancient writings and, by the time of his death in Year 55 of his father's reign, he had systematically restored the Old Kingdom pyramids at Giza and Saqqara which, even then, were more than a thousand years old.

Khaemwase, dressed as a high priest, kneels beside an image of Memphis' god, Ptah-Tatenen. From Memphis.

Ramesses II erected a stela chapel (right) at Gebel Silsileh in honor of Hapi, god of the Nile flood. Sety I's virtually identical monument may be seen to the left.

As part of the celebration of his jubilee festival, Ramesses II ran around a course four times to symbolize his taking possession of the land. From Beit el Wali.

The King Divine and Eternal

In Ramesses the Great's Egypt, as decade followed decade, peace and prosperity prevailed. Ramesses II was increasingly concerned with establishing himself as a god in the eyes of his people and ensuring that he would live and rule forever.

Through the traditional jubilee festival *(hebsed)*, beginning in Year 30, he sought to renew his youthfulness and power. The jubilee was celebrated (in theory, at least) only after a king had occupied the throne for 30 years. It was then repeated approximately every three years thereafter. The jubilee reinvigorated the aging monarch, reaffirmed his right to rule and re-enacted his coronation. For the subjects of Ramesse the Great, it was a new experience, since almost 100 years had passed since a traditional jubilee was last celebrated (in the long reign of Amunhotep III). Ramesses II would eventually celebrate 14 jubilees, more than any other king in Egypt's history.

For several months before his first jubilee festival in 1249 B.C., the king's son, Khaemwase, in his role as high priest of Memphis, must have traveled the land proclaiming the great event. Records of his announcement, in the form of stelae and inscriptions, are found particularly in Egypt's southern border areas, namely, Aswan, where it was believed the Nile floods began, and Gebel Silsileh, an area sacred to Hapi, god of the Nile flood. In a sense, the jubilee was similar to a flood, for just as the Nile's deposit of fertile silt rejuvenated the land, so too did his jubilee festival rejuvenate the king. In fact, Ramesses the Great boasted later that the Nile flood rose especially high at that time. (Supporting evidence, however, is lacking.)

Exactly where the king celebrated his jubilees is unclear. Whether the first was in Memphis or perhaps at Pi-Ramesses, large crowds must have gathered to witness the event. When the time arrived, the thirtieth anniversary of the king's accession, a procession formed. Ramesses the Great, dressed in a knee-length cloak and followed by priests and high officials, entered a special temple precinct. There, he gave gifts to the gods, and they responded by granting him hundreds of thousands of years of rule and by renewing *Ma'at*, society's divine order. To demonstrate his triumph and renewal and to symbolize his taking possession of the land, the king then sprinted around a special track. This was followed by singing, dancing, feasting and all manner of joyous celebration.

After his second jubilee festival, Ramesses II made another addition to his name, explaining that he was "Lord of Jubilees, like his father Ptah-Tatenen." Not only did Ramesses II associate himself with Egypt's gods, but he had now become one of them in his own eyes. In Nubia, especially, where he enjoyed greatest independence from Egypt's priesthood, his deification was proclaimed repeatedly.

In his later years the king spent much of his time at Pi-Ramesses. From there he saw Egypt's cities grow, her temples thrive and her people prosper. His peace with the Hittites continued, despite great changes in the Ancient Near East, and the world paid him homage. As jubilee followed jubilee, the divine promise of hundreds of thousands of years appeared to be coming true. Ramesses II would outlive not only many of his wives, but also his first 12 sons!

II
Egypt in the Ramesside Age

Gods of the Nile flood hold Egypt's
riches at the temple of Ramesses II
at Abydos.

The goddess Isis suckles the young Ramesses II. From Beit el Wali.

Ran sits Am deir rep Fro

Ramesses II pays homage to his own image included (second from right) among the gods at Wadi Sebua.

Villagers worshiped awesome images of Ramesses the Great. From Luxor.

As visitors to today's Egypt soon realize, Ramesses II's huge stone buildings still mark the landscape at almost every ancient site. Temples he erected, statuary he commissioned, monuments he inscribed and the funerary temple and royal tomb he built for himself all provide first-hand information about his life and his world, as he wished posterity to know them. However, the fascination that Egyptian civilization holds for us stems not just from the splendor of monuments and the glory of kings. It comes also from evidence that our ancient counterparts grappled with moral, ethical and practical concerns similar to ours and evolved explanations and solutions that have, in many cases, maintained their validity over the millennia.

Such evidence is found in the mudbrick remains of the cities Ramesses II built—palaces, public buildings, workshops, the houses of citizens and the remains of their material possessions. It also still exists in copious archival records on papyrus (ancient paper made from the stem of the plant flattened and pressed together, as Cat. No. 23) and on scraps of inscribed limestone or pottery known as ostraca (Cat. Nos. 53 and 57). These reveal the minutiae of everyday life—prices and wages, lawsuits, marriages and divorces, farm production, taxes, labor problems. Such information reflects the people's hopes and fears and their relation to their gods.

Worship of the Gods

Ramesses II lived in a divine land. Happiness on earth and eternal life in the netherworld, for king and commoner alike, depended directly upon the care and attention lavished on the myriad gods who oversaw Egypt's proper functioning. On a cosmic sphere, different gods represented and controlled the sun, moon, sky, earth, air and Nile flood. Each city also had its own local god or gods responsible for the well-being of its citizenry and often credited with its creation. When cities gained particular prominence politically, as Pi-Ramesses, Memphis and Thebes did in Ramesses II's Egypt, their local gods grew in prestige and power. Average villagers had little access to these awesome state gods, so on a daily basis, they worshiped more intimate, more approachable gods who saw specifically to their needs.

The king presented still another avenue for prayer and personal worship. The office of kingship was divine. Ramesses II, like every other Egyptian king, was the product of the union between a heavenly father and an earthly mother. Goddesses suckled him and supervised his upbringing. Certain named statues of him represented Ramesses II's kingly office deified, and they, too, were regarded as divine. The colossal statues of him that stood in pairs outside temples throughout the land acted as intermediaries between passers-by and the great gods at home inside. Pious villagers and high officials alike might offer a petition or erect a stela to the cult of the king. In this manner, Ramesses the Great, deified, was benefactor to all. (On occasion, Ramesses II, the mortal, is himself shown worshiping a statue of Ramesses II, the god!)

What the gods had created, the king inherited. Ramesses II's duty was to preserve the union of Upper and Lower Egypt which was secured in his name. He did this by defeating Egypt's enemies, defined as the forces of chaos, and by honoring the gods. In almost every ancient city, Ramesses II built new temples to the local deities or added to existing ones.

Egyptian temples, as homes of the gods, replicated the legendary structure of the universe at the time of creation. A mudbrick enclosure wall separated the sacred area inside—the primeval hill which rose from a watery chaos at the beginning of time,

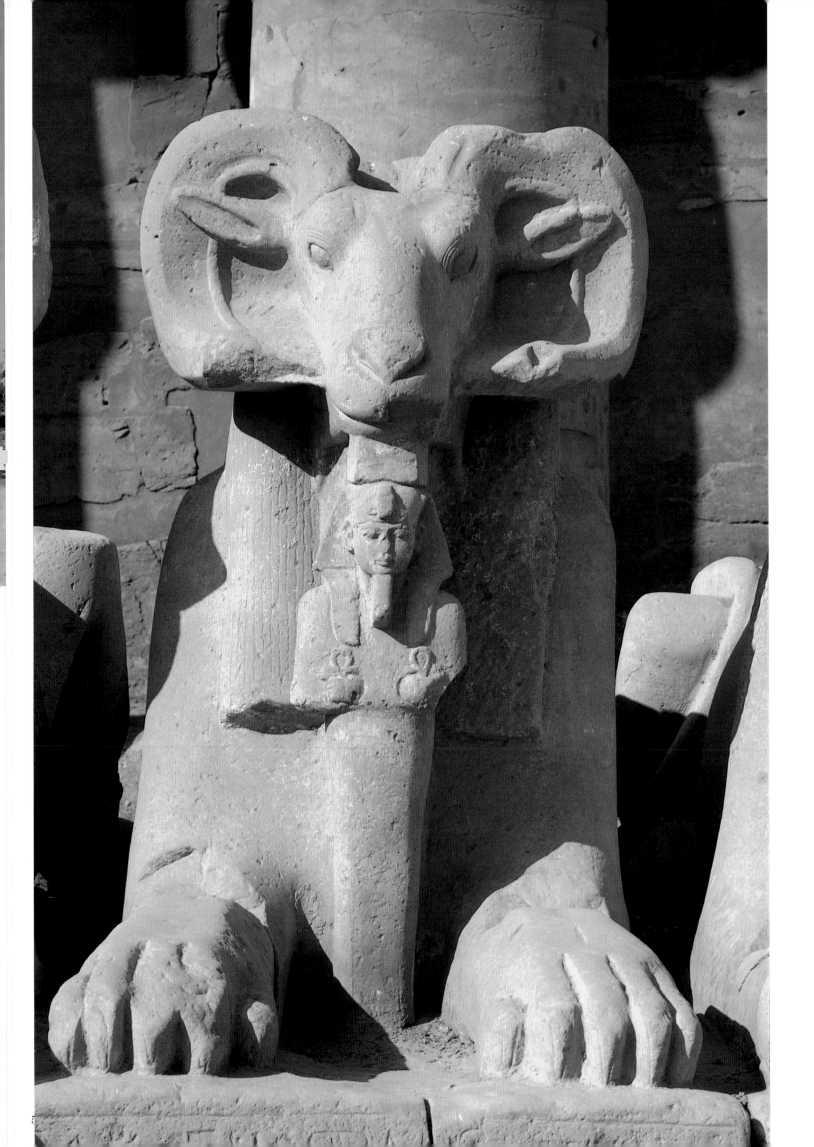

The ram of Amun protects an image
of Ramesses II. From Karnak.

Ramesses II erected an avenue of
ram-headed sphinxes leading to the
temple of Karnak.

At the "Temple of Ramesses, Beloved of Amun, Hearer of Prayer" at Karnak's east gate, passers-by prayed to statues of the king so that he might speak on their behalf to the gods at home inside.

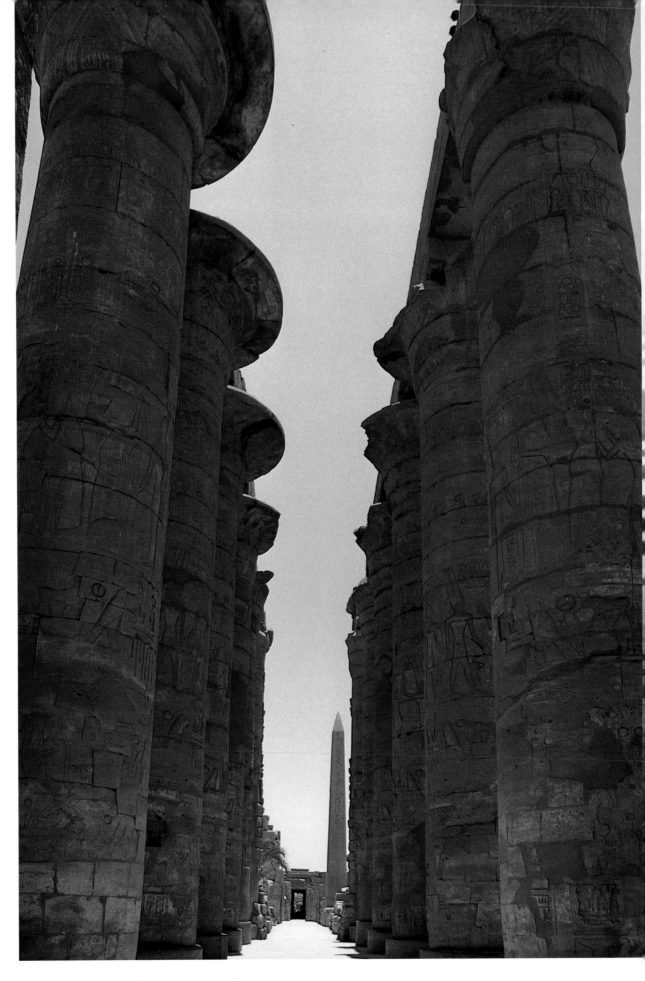

134 columns arranged in 16 rows
form the hypostyle hall at Karnak.
This architectural masterwork, the
largest hall of columns in the world,
occupies an area of 53,800 square
feet.

Wadi Sebua at its original site in Nubia. The temple is dedicated to Amun, Ra-Horakhty and Ramesses II.

Sphinxes at Wadi Sebua in Nubia bear the head of Ramesses the Great wearing the double crown. "Sebua" is Arabic for lion.

In Egypt proper—that is, the Delta and Nile Valley (to Aswan)—Ramesses II's self-glorifying activities and the image he presented were governed by tradition and were held in check by powerful temple clergy. However, in far-off Nubia, the 800-mile stretch of land south of Aswan, no such constraints applied. No major Nubian town or strategically significant area was left untouched as Ramesses II built anew or embellished over a dozen temples. In Nubia, especially in the many temples completed after his second jubilee, Ramesses the Great became a resident deity.

Many of Ramesses II's Nubian temples are familiar to us because of international efforts, during the building of the Aswan High Dam in the 1960s, to record and or move them to higher ground before they were covered by rising waters. The list includes Beit el Wali, Gerf Hussein, Wadi Sebua, Derr, Abu Simbel, Amara West and Aksha. These southern temples replicated most elements of sanctuaries throughout Egypt proper, and they typically incorporated hard sandstone from the Nubian cliffs as part of their matrix. Often the hypostyle hall was cut into the face of the cliff, and the holy of holies, the shrine housing cult statues of the temple's resident gods, was carved deeper still into the mountain. The Nubian temples were exceptional in the integration of colossal royal images into their architecture. Sphinxes bearing Ramesses the Great's features guarded the entryways; statues of him *en masse* served as pillars; and he resided among other gods as their equal in the holy of holies. Made by local artisans, these statues often replaced in volume what they lacked in sophistication.

Perhaps the most famous of Ramesses II's Nubian projects—the two temples on the Nile's west bank that are cut deep into the sandstone cliffs at Abu Simbel—is also his greatest achievement. These temples now lie 215 feet higher than they did when Ramesses II first commissioned the work, probably sometime after his fifth regnal year. His original purpose was to honor Egypt's major gods and their local Nubian variants. However, as the impressive images of himself were carved on the facade and pillars of the first temple and its walls were covered with a record of his military exploits, Ramesses the Great's ideas about who he was began to change. He ordered artisans to re-carve scenes of the gods at the back of the first hall to include himself. From the second hall back, he receives prominence equal to that of his fellow gods. In the end, the main temple at Abu Simbel, completed sometime after the king's 35th regnal year, became a temple to Ramesses the Great. He called it "The House of Ramesses, Beloved of Amun."

The image of the goddess Mut was moved to the right so a representation of Ramesses II might be added to a row of gods. From Abu Simbel.

Osiride pillars in the hypostyle hall leading to the sanctuary at Abu Simbel.

Opposite page. Ramesses the Great with his family at his feet from his temple at Abu Simbel.

The temples of Abu Simbel at their new site above the waters of Lake Nasser.

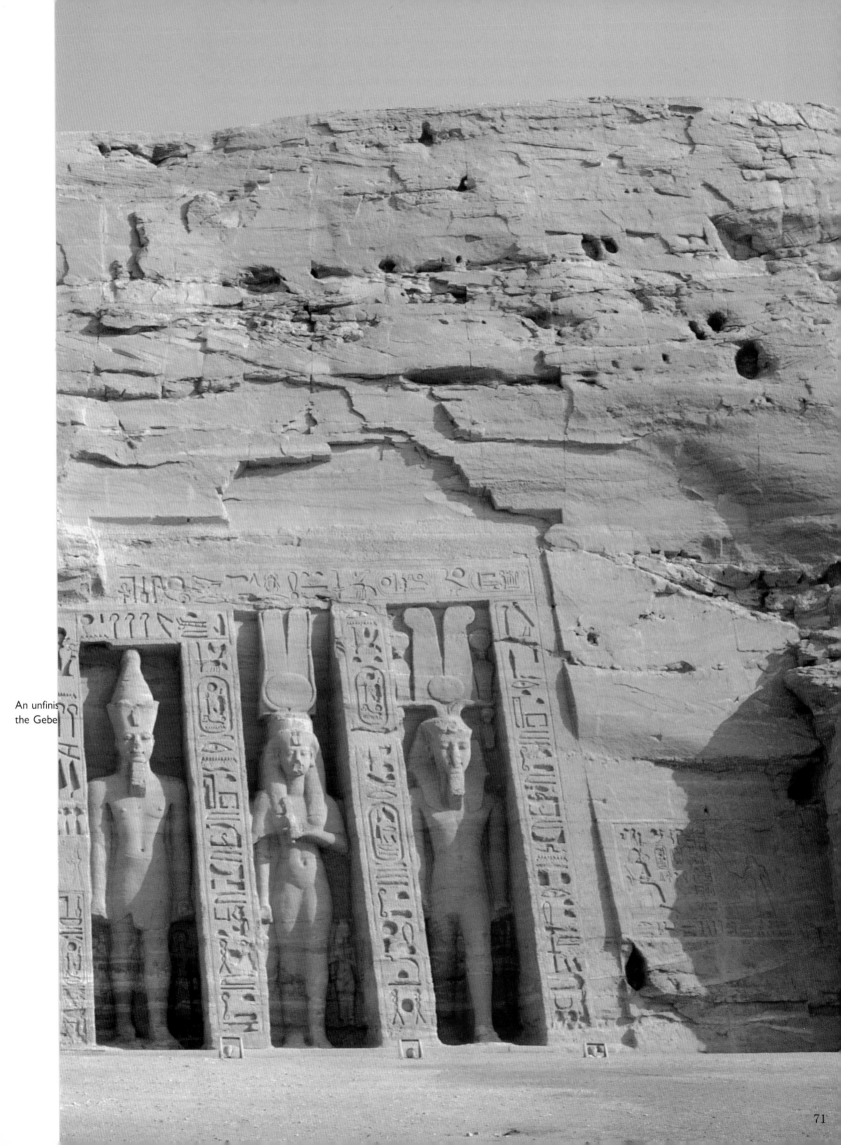

An unfinis
the Gebe

In all the mining, quarrying and building operations, Ramesses the Great himself took an active and proud interest. In an inscription on the Luxor temple, he relates how, after he had pored over ancient records, "the writings of the House of Life," to learn "the secrets of heaven and all the mysteries of earth,"[10] he then conceived a plan: "Look ye, I have it in my mind to perform construction work for my father Amun-Ra."[11] He assembled his workmen and overseers, and he tells us, "the king himself issued instructions for conducting the work."[12] The fruits of this labor remain as proof not only of the power of Ramesses II's regency, but also of the productiveness of his quarrying operations and the skill of his stonemasons and sculptors.

The Egyptians divided stone into categories based on appearance, hardness and place of origin. Beds of sandstone, the lightest and softest of Ramesses II's primary building materials, were found in Esna (34 miles south of Thebes) upriver into Nubia, where his temples were carved directly into the sandstone cliffs. Sandstone for Ramesses II's other temples, statues, obelisks or sphinxes, usually came from Gebel Silsileh, about 95 miles south of Thebes. These quarries, still worked until the nineteenth century, produced the lofty columns of Karnak's hypostyle hall and its avenue of sphinxes. Mistakes made in the preliminary carving stages of several of the sphinxes forced Ramesses II's stone carvers to abandon these works in the quarry, where they may still be seen today.

Limestone, slightly heavier than sandstone and similarly easy to quarry and sculpt, was found in beds extending from Cairo upriver to Esna. The quarries at Tura, about ten miles north of Memphis, provided most of the high quality building stone for the ancient capital, and for Saqqara, its chief necropolis. Much of this stone later became building material for medieval Cairo or fuel for its lime kilns, so comparatively little remains.

Granite, heavier and harder than sandstone or limestone, was correspondingly more difficult to quarry, transport and carve and was rarely used in temple construction except as door jambs, lintels or column bases. Nevertheless, granite obelisks, stelae and statues bearing Ramesses II's name abound, despite the difficulty involved in its handling. The area around Aswan was Ramesses II's chief source of both black and pink granite, and he claimed considerable expertise in its acquisition. During Sety I's ninth regnal year, when Ramesses II was probably barely a teenager, one of his duties was to supervise for his father the quarrying and transport of "very great obelisks and great and marvelous statues"[13] from Aswan. Later, in Year 8 of his own reign, he returned to Aswan to select stone for his own projects. A stela inscription tells how he then reported to his stonemasons that he had "examined a fine mountain in order that I might give you the use of it."[14]

Ramesses has also left us an account of his discovery of a large deposit of quartzite, one of the hardest and heaviest of the common Egyptian building stones which was used infrequently, due mostly to the comparatively small amount available. It was obtained from the Gebel Ahmar quarries just northeast of Cairo. Nevertheless, Ramesses the Great, while out for a stroll one day in the desert outside Heliopolis (near Gebel Ahmar), came upon a great quantity of quartzite, "the like of which had never been found since the beginning of time."[15] From this enormous block of stone "higher than a granite obelisk,"[16] his artisans carved a divine statue of the king which was erected in Pi-Ramesses. Unfortunately, this tantalizing inscription is the only evidence we have today of its existence.

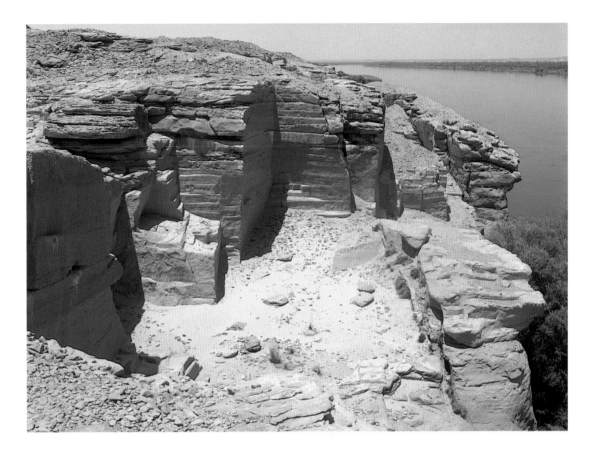

The quarries at Gebel Silsileh provided sandstone for building projects from pharaonic times until the twentieth century A.D.

Perhaps a flaw in the stone caused quarrymen to abandon this colossal statue in the Aswan granite quarries.

Comparatively little is known about the many quarrying expeditions which took place during Ramesses II's rule. We may assume, however, that they were similar to a later expedition that set forth under royal auspices during the reign of Ramesses IV (1154-1148 B.C.), when High Priest of Amun Ramesses-nakht (Cat. No 7) led a granite-quarrying gang of 8,362 men and overseers to Wadi Hammamat in the Eastern Desert. Such quarry missions required the efforts of skilled specialists, untrained laborers, stone movers, tool sharpeners, baggage handlers, provision suppliers and errand runners. Quarry sites must have looked like small towns, equipped with temples, administrative buildings, processing areas and huts for workers whose job it was to turn mountains into building blocks cut to exact specifications for each project.

Quarrying methods were well-defined. Copper chisels, wooden mallets and heavy stone balls were used to pound out trenches in the rock around all four sides of the desired area and to drive wooden wedges beneath it. When moistened, the wedges expanded and helped to detach the block from the stone below. Finer finishing was done by skilled personnel using more delicate chisels, adzes, mallets and rubbing stones, aided by cubit rods (Cat. No. 11), right angles (Cat. No. 9) and plumb lines (Cat. No. 10). Ships and barges then transported the blocks to workshops and building sites where artisans and architects enjoyed working conditions decidedly more comfortable than those at the quarry! There the intense rays of the sun bouncing off

According to Ramesses II, he rewarded his quarrymen with all manner of succulent foods.

desert cliffs often sent temperatures soaring above 140° Fahrenheit, making the quarryman's life all but intolerable for a good part of the year. Hard manual labor under such conditions clearly caused high fatality rates. Ramesses IV's expedition to Wadi Hammamat lost over 900 men!

Still, Ramesses II would like us to believe that he treated his workmen well and that "their hearts were happy, their arms strong." [17] His quarrymen, he relates, were provided with clothing, sandals and ointment. They received excellent care, ample reward and feasted on cakes, wine, bread, barley, fish and beans. (Sagely he comments that workers perform best "when the belly is satisfied." [18]) Despite the king's humanitarian claims, it must be concluded that his myriad building projects, by their very number and size, involved the exploitation of many laborers. Some of the

Forty overseers were each required to deliver 2,000 bricks according to the inscription on a roll of leather written in Ramesses II's fifth regnal year.

workers were clearly foreign captives or prisoners forced to serve their terms doing hard labor.

Among them, in all probability, were a group of Near Easterners, the Hebrews who, according to the Bible, fled servitude in the land of Goshen (Egypt's fertile Eastern Delta region). As related in the Book of Exodus, the Hebrews, led by Moses, escaped from Egypt by crossing the Red Sea (probably the Reed Sea, a marshy area near the Sinai border). Pharaoh's pursuing charioteers, intent on preventing the flight of so many skilled laborers, were drowned in their attempt to follow them through the water. The Bible also tells us that Moses and his followers then wandered for 40 years in the Sinai desert, overcoming hardship after hardship, before finally making their way to a new homeland in the land of Canaan on the shores of the Eastern Mediterranean.

The Egyptians in their writings make no mention of this event, but in view of the propagandistic nature of ancient Egyptian official histories (including, of course, those of Ramesses II), this omission of the Exodus is understandable. What became a central event in the history of the nation of Israel was probably only a minor annoyance to mighty Egypt. Indeed, in ancient Egyptian records, the people of Israel are mentioned only once, on a stela inscribed in Year 5 of the reign of Ramesses II's son and successor, Merneptah. Erected in commemoration of a victory over the Libyans, the so-called ''Israel Stela'' also lists all the cities and tribes in Syria and Canaan that Merneptah had similarly defeated. The fact that Israel is so listed provides clear (and significant) evidence that by the fifth year after the death of Ramesses II, the desert wanderings of the people of Israel had ended. Assuming 40 years for these wanderings, if the Exodus took place at least 40 years prior to the Israel Stela and no more than 71 (66 years of Ramesses II's rule plus five years of Merneptah's), then the departure from Egypt would have occurred during Ramesses the Great's regency. Accordingly, Ramesses the Great and Moses may have been contemporaries.

Egypt's bustling cities and splendid temples made her prosperity visible. Since silver, copper and gold were mediums of exchange, the weight and amount of her precious metal resources made Egypt's wealth quantifiable. (Coinage was not yet in use and would not exist in Egypt until the end of Pharaonic times in the fourth century B.C.)

Prior to the New Kingdom, silver's rarity had made it highly prized, but in Ramesses II's day it arrived in such quantity as tribute from Asia, Crete and Libya that it was only half as valuable as gold. The value of copper was about 1/100th that of silver during Ramesses II's rule, and it came chiefly from Sinai, Syria and Cyprus. Copper's abundance and the ease with which it could be mined led to its wide use in everything from weaponry to cooking pots.

Glistening, corrosion-proof and malleable, gold was the most precious metal. Its value far transcended its exchange rate. Because it brought to mind the imperishable sun and its radiant life-giving qualities, gold was identified with the gods, and gold mining was a privilege reserved for kings and for temples. Most gold entered Egypt from Nubia as tribute. Although we lack production figures, we know the mines of Wawat, in Lower Nubia between the Nile's First and Second Cataracts, and those of Kush, farther upriver between the Second and Fourth Cataracts, were among the most productive. The Wadi Hammamat mines in Egypt proper also yielded gold.

On the ''Israel Stela,'' King Merneptah lists Israel among Egypt's conquered peoples.

The world's earliest map shows the location of the gold mines of Wadi Hammamat.

77

The Biblical Land of Goshen refers to the fertile Eastern Delta regions.

The Sinai desert at Mount Sinai.

Gold mining, like stone quarrying, was a difficult task. Gold mining gangs probably resembled quarry gangs, consisting mostly of prisoners of war, criminals and soldiers, as well as policemen who made sure they did not escape. Gold lay both in veins within the quartz rock and in alluvial gravels washed into long dry river beds or *wadis*. To separate metal from stone, the rocks and gravels had to be excavated with heavy tools, crushed into powder and then washed.

One of the main problems confronting a gold mining expedition was the lack of water. In one instance during Ramesses II's reign, the shortage was so severe in the desert regions of Wawat that half the expedition's men and animals died of thirst before they even reached the mines! Well aware that fewer workers meant lower yields, but knowing also that during Sety I's rule, in this same area, miners had dug down 200 feet without finding water, Ramesses II summoned the princes of the court and asked for ideas. His Viceroy of Kush suggested that Ramesses II himself pray to Hapi (god of the Nile flood), "Let water be brought upon the mountain."[19] Hapi would heed Ramesses' plea, the Viceroy assured him, "because all the gods love you more than any king."[20] Recognizing good advice, Ramesses II gave it a try, and behold, a mere 20 feet down, his workers struck water!

After the miners reduced tons of rock to powder from which they retrieved the gold dust, it was smelted into easily transportable units and brought to Egypt in bars, rings or lumps. Scribes carefully weighed and recorded it, and it finally found its way to the treasure houses and workshops of the king and the gods.

Egyptian gold in its natural state ranged between 17 and 22 carats. To produce treasures for the gods or the royal family, or golden gifts for trusted officials who had distinguished themselves in Pharaoh's service, craftsmen melted the gold (at a heat of 1945° Fahrenheit) in a blast furnace fueled by wood and dung and stoked by means of a foot-operated bellows. Goldsmiths then cast the molten metal in molds, hammered it into sheets, drew it out into wire, cut it into strips, formed it into granules (Cat. No. 49) or mixed it with other elements which added color or strength. With solder (made from a copper salt and gum or from a gold alloy) they could produce a joint that was almost invisible (Cat. Nos. 62, 69 and 70). Alternatively, they might use gold rivets (Cat. No. 64). Wielding tiny chisels and mallets, the gold workers engraved, embossed, chased and hammered designs and inscriptions into plain surfaces. They used brightly colored stones or glass set into cloisons (dividing bands) to add interest, to jewelry especially (Cat. No. 49). Beautifully fashioned golden vessels enabled the gods to eat and drink in style (Cat. Nos. 63, 64, 66, 69 and 70). They fashioned awesome ceremonial weapons, and their sheet gold coverings made temple doors, walls, obelisks and columns glisten.

Delicate and beautiful, masterpieces created by these artisans over 3,000 years ago are as appealing to us today as they must have been to their original owners. The reign of Ramesses the Great, thanks to them, was indeed a golden age.

old chalices, libation vessels, and offering dishes testify to the riches of Ramesses the Great's temple at Abydos.

Governance of the Kingdom

Ramesses the Great ruled an estimated 3,000,000 people in Egypt proper, and his jurisdiction over Nubia and the Levant added another few million, according to one demographic estimate. The well-being of all his subjects was the king's responsibility, to be fulfilled, in theory, with divine assistance. In practice, he relied on a multi-branched administrative structure established in rudimentary form at the beginning of dynastic Egyptian history (ca. 3200 B.C.).

By Dynasty XIX, the Egyptian administration had evolved into a complex bureaucracy which may be divided into four branches: royal court, temple, military and civil service. Each branch had its own responsibilities and hierarchy, but each reported ultimately to the king. In Ramesses the Great's Egypt, the king always maintained control.

The large palaces Ramesses II built for himself in major cities—Pi-Ramesses, Memphis, Thebes—were far more than just residential quarters. Often they included a complex of government offices, reception areas, archives, storerooms, workrooms, stables, stockyards, breweries, bakeries, kitchens, military marshalling areas, ornamental gardens, pleasure lakes and perhaps a harbor. The king, his wives and children, his trusted officials and their families would have occupied the palace's living areas. Royal lands provided food and income to supplement tribute and taxes. Artisans' studios and cottage industries supplied immediate needs.

Remains of the audience hall and throne room from the palace of Ramesses II at the Ramesseum.

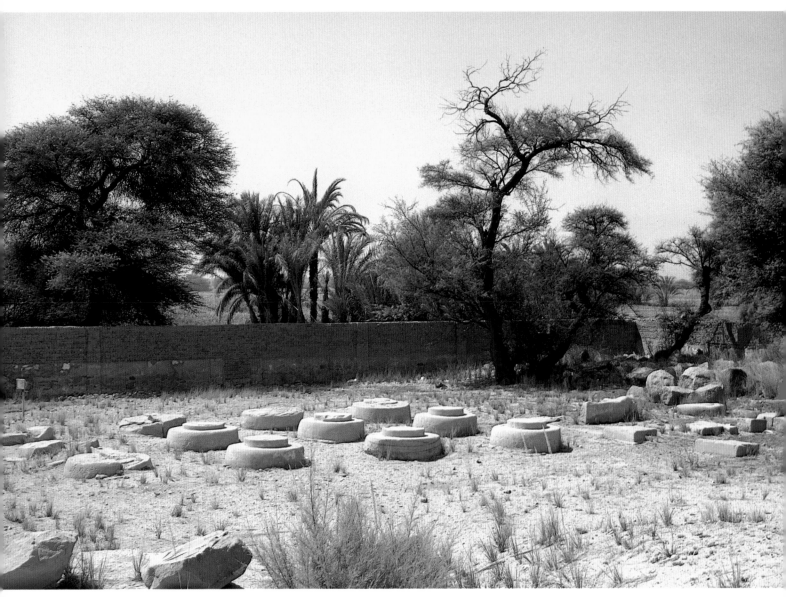

Each palace compound had its own administrative staff. Chief stewards coordinated the efforts of scribes, bakers, brewers, cooks, butlers, gardeners, overseers, farm laborers, herdsmen, stable masters, guards, artisans, nurses, weavers, tutors, messengers and body servants. When the king traveled, his personal entourage included such specialists as cup bearer, sandal bearer, sunshade bearer and fan bearer. (Their duties were probably more ceremonial than physically demanding.)

How splendid these edifices must have been in Ramesses II's day. Since they were intended for use only during the king's life on earth—his eternal dwelling place would be in the Valley of the Kings—they were built mainly of mud brick, an impermanent material. Today little remains, apart from some brightly colored faience tiles, which once adorned the walls and floors of his magnificent palace at Pi-Ramesses (Cat. Nos. 30-34), and stone column bases and mudbrick foundations from a less imposing palace within the sacred precinct of his mortuary temple, the Ramesseum. Ramesses II built certain smaller palaces to serve as short-term resting places so that he could conduct business and receive visitors at select temples such as the Ramesseum (the construction of which had begun almost immediately after his coronation).

Some clues to the way the royal court functioned are found in the remains of the Ramesseum palace. Though miniscule in comparison to the vast acreage of Ramesses II's major palaces, its layout, displaying a clear division between public and private areas, was probably characteristic of all his residences. Behind a square reception area, filled with 16 columns arranged in rows of four, lay a smaller, square, four-columned room with a dais where the enthroned king might greet high officials. Auxiliary rooms for ritual or storage surrounded the complex. Far to the rear and inaccessible from the public areas lay four small housing units. On ceremonial occasions Ramesses II might ascend a stairway to a balcony overlooking the temple's open court. From this lofty ''window of appearance'' he could address his subjects or present awards. The Ramesseum palace also played a role in Ramesses II's funeral ceremonies.

Leaning down from the window of appearance, King Sety I presents Hormin with the Gold of Valor necklaces. From Saqqara.

Living quarters for great royal wives, lesser wives, children, servants and administrators occupied substantial space within palace districts. The harem was not just a residential area. Here young princes, princesses and children of high officials learned reading, writing, politics and leadership, manners and morals. Foreign princes sent their children here (sometimes unwillingly) to receive training in the Egyptian way of life. Virtually an independent institution, the harem had its own administrative staff and its own cottage industries, including weaving, farming and herding.

While court officials attended to the concerns of the State (i.e., the king), temple personnel similarly cared for the gods and their holdings. Like the State, temples owned fields, gardens, animals, workyards, storehouses, boats, slaves, mineral wealth, even entire market towns, all of which required large administrative and maintenance staffs. Most temple precincts also included wayside chapels, archives, artisans' studios, schools and living quarters.

The high priest of each temple served as its supreme authority in the absence of the king. (The high priest of Amun at Karnak wielded considerable power, since Karnak was one of the main employers in New Kingdom Egypt.) Second, third and fourth priests or prophets aided the high priest in attending to the god's intimate needs. A temple's lesser priests performed other duties, such as reciting liturgy, burning incense, pouring libations, celebrating special festivals, collecting offerings, maintaining records and tracking the passage of time so that each ritual might be performed at its specified day and hour (Cat. No. 54). There were also lay *(wab)* priests

who served for one month at a time, three times a year. During their period of duty, they, like full-time priests, were obliged to shave their entire bodies, refrain from wearing wool clothing and remain sexually abstinent. Women of the New Kingdom aided their gods primarily as singers, dancers and musicians, although occasionally they attained higher priestly office as well. Meryetamun, daughter and later wife of Ramesses II, served as Sistrum Player for Mut, Menat Player for Hathor, Songstress of Atum and Dancer for Horus (Cat. No. 2).

A temple's riches came largely from royal gifts presented by kings to curry divine favor and priestly support. In exchange, kings hoped to obtain what only the gods could give—long life, dominion, health and general prosperity. Over the years a temple might accumulate enormous wealth. By Dynasty XX, for example, fully 10% of Egypt's agricultural land belonged to the sanctuary of Amun at Karnak.

In many respects, houses of gods in Ramesside Egypt resembled semi-autonomous corporations. One temple might lease land to another or open it to sharecroppers. Temple-owned ships transported goods from its market towns. Surpluses might be traded, but despite their vast power, temple priests remained subordinate to the king. Before any income in the form of produce, grain, wines, oil, precious stones and metals, cloth and handiwork went into temple storerooms, a share went to the king as tax. Not even the gods were exempt!

To ensure that the king's voice would remain supreme was the task of the military. A standing army had existed in Egypt only since the beginning of the New Kingdom (ca. 1550 B.C.), when it was established to protect newly conquered territories. By Dynasty XIX, it had grown considerably.

The king was indisputable commander-in-chief of the army, and we know Ramesses II took his role seriously. Generals, usually princes, commanded each division of about 5000 men and reported to the king. Each division, consisting of infantry and chariotry regiments of about 200 to 250 men under the leadership of a commander or standard bearer, was further subdivided into platoons of 50. The smallest units of his army were squads of ten men each.

To recruit troops for the army's mainstay, the infantry, army scribes traveled from village to village promising young farm boys adventure, foreign plunder and a chance to better their lot if they became soldiers. Teachers, meanwhile, fearful that children of noble families might also be seduced into joining the army, instructed their pupils about the reality of a military life. According to a New Kingdom papyrus: ''The soldier, that much tormented one...is taken when yet a child to be imprisoned in a barrack.''[21] In training, ''he is beaten like papyrus and battered with castigation.''[22] On the march, ''his bread and water are upon his shoulder like the load of an ass...he drinks of smelly water and halts (only) to keep watch.''[23] In battle, ''he is like a plucked bird...Turn back,'' the teachers warned, ''from the soldier's calling.''[24] When army recruiters failed to produce sufficient inductees for Pharaoh's army, they resorted to conscription. Foreign mercenaries and prisoners of war also joined the ranks of the military.

Ramesses II's troops fought valiantly for him (most of the time). Archers led the way into battle, followed by soldiers armed with axes, swords, daggers and spears and protected by shields, helmets and sometimes coats of mail. Chariots, made of wood with bronze and leather trappings, protected each flank and the rear. Charioteers

Ramesses II's High Priest of Amun Bakenkhonsu. He probably usurped this statue from an official of Dynasty XVIII. From Karnak.

Sennedjem plows and his wife
scatters seed in a painting from their
tomb at Deir el Medina.

Sennedjem cuts grain with a sickle,
and his wife collects the ears in her
basket. From Deir el Medina.

heaps, measured, recorded and returned to farmers, less the amount due tax assessors. Flax plants had to be harvested near the root so the precious fibers would not suffer damage. After seeds were detached for next years' planting, the stalks were transformed into linen thread from which was woven the cloth most commonly worn by Egyptians, rich and poor. (In the hot Egyptian climate, wool was too warm, and silk and cotton came to Egypt only in Ptolemaic and Roman times respectively.)

Even with the land's fertility guaranteed yearly by the silt-bearing flood waters, the lot of the farmer was difficult. One late New Kingdom school text asked young readers to consider the plight of the "cultivator" in whose fields "mice abound, the locust descends, the cattle devour (and) sparrows bring want" and who still had to pay his harvest-tax "after the snake has carried off one-half and the hippopotamus has eaten up the rest." [26]

On desert fringes beyond the agricultural lands, lay animal grazing land. Oxen and cattle, bulls, pigs, sheep, goats and donkeys were raised for work and for food. Animals less domestic, including ibex, oryx, gazelle and antelope might also be trapped for game parks and the gods' offering tables. Wild fowl—at least 14 species have been identified—were captured and raised for food and for aviaries of wealthy estate owners. In addition, New Kingdom Egypt witnessed the arrival of the domestic chicken. Imagine an owner's delight, watching these wonderful birds lay an egg every day!

Farms and herds fed and clothed Egypt's people, but towns and cities, located usually on the floodplain but high enough to escape flood waters, formed her cultural hubs. A few cities were planned, among them Tell el Amarna, Pi-Ramesses, Nubian garrison areas and Deir el Medina, a village near the Valley of the Kings built to provide homes for workmen constructing the royal tombs. These planned cities often display an axial layout of streets and houses, with various sectors devoted to separate concentrations of administrative buildings, temples, crafts and industries, markets or living quarters. Most towns, however, spread irregularly on the basis of need and availability of land. In many instances, they grew up around the estates their inhabitants served.

In residential areas, larger houses were grouped together in affluent "suburbs," while smaller domiciles in poorer sections shared contiguous walls. Most families had to make do with modest mudbrick dwellings of three or four rooms laid out one behind the other, like the typical Deir el Medina home. A foyer, entered from the street, led to a larger room with a low platform to one side for eating or sleeping and a false door stela for worship set into the wall. One or two plastered wood columns supported a flat wooden roof, and light was admitted through tiny windows just below the ceiling. A short flight of steps led down to a household storage area. Behind the "living room" lay a sleeping area containing a bed niche. Food was prepared on the roof or at the rear of the house in an open air "kitchen" which generally contained a clay oven and a recessed mortar for grinding grain. Throughout the house, plastered mudbrick floors and walls might be painted with images of favorite deities, floral friezes or simple bands of color.

On the whole, furniture was sparse and utilitarian. People sat on high- or low-back chairs and stools and ate at low tables from a variety of plates, bowls, saucers, pitchers and cups made primarily of undecorated, wheel-thrown pottery. At night, reed mats or beds with woven cord "springs" provided comfort. Padded headrests

Cattle grew fat from the bounty of the land. From the temple of Ramesses II at Abydos.

Padded reed mats placed in niches often served as beds for Deir el Medina villagers.

Deir el Medina kitchens included sunken hearths for cooking. Walls throughout the houses were often plastered and white-washed.

py ar
in Rar
offeri
of a p
Deir

Desolate cliffs in the Valley of the
Kings hid the tombs of New
Kingdom royalty.

III
Quest for Immortality

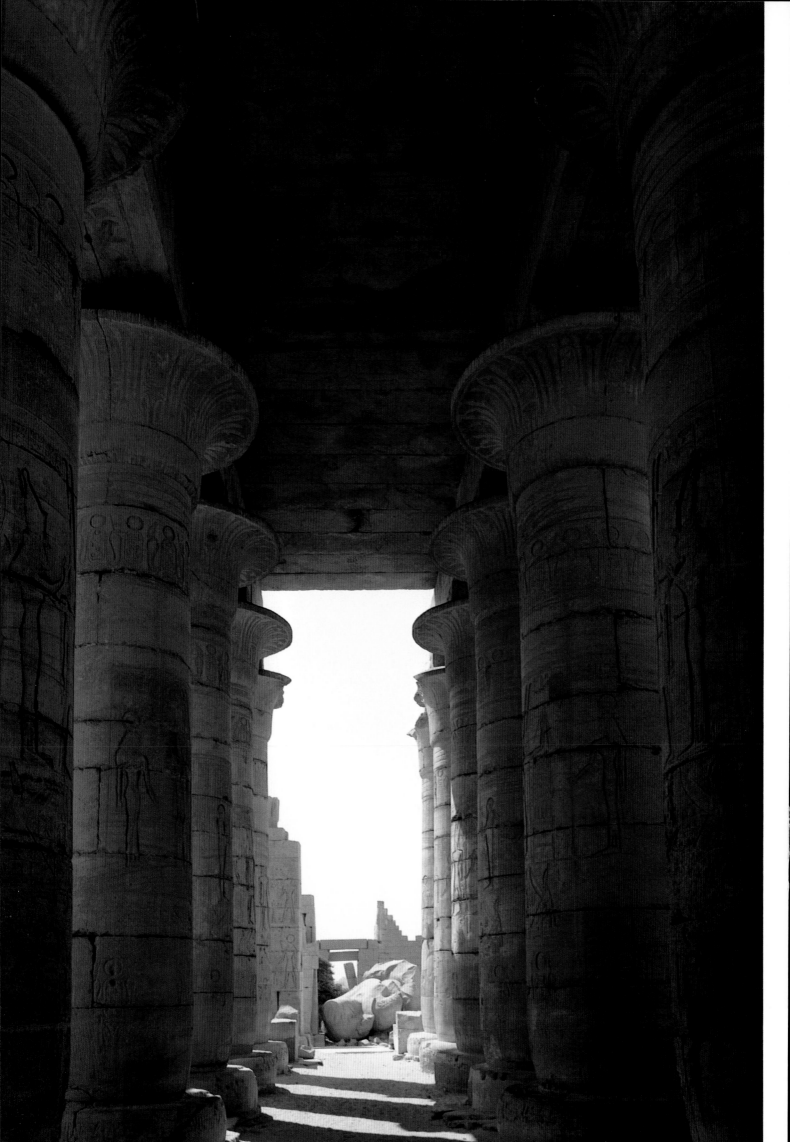

To ancient Egyptians, an ideal life on earth lasted 110 years. If proper conditions were met, death was not an end but a beginning—the start of a journey into an other-worldly realm of everlasting bliss. Ramesses the Great, living well into his ninth decade, was on his way to achieving the ideal, for he had expended considerable resources and manpower to guarantee his immortality.

Early in his reign, he had begun to make careful preparations for his death, burial and entry into eternity to join his fellow gods. Like his New Kingdom predecessors, Ramesses chose sites in Western Thebes for the majestic mortuary temple where his funeral ceremonies were to be held and for the royal tomb where he would be buried. Heeding lessons learned millennia earlier, he located his temple, the Ramesseum, at the desert's edge, on the opposite side of the limestone cliffs from the *wadi*, known as the Valley of the Kings, where his tomb would be hidden. This was to draw attention away from his burial place and ensure its security against violation and plunder. Or so he thought. Work on both temple and tomb began almost immediately after Ramesses II assumed the throne.

Looking down the papyrus columns of the hypostyle hall at the Ramesseum.

The king's cult lived on in his funerary temple, the Ramesseum.

An Eternal Dwelling Place

The Ramesseum was designed to be a splendid eternal dwelling place where the cult of the king would be honored in perpetuity. The spot Ramesses chose to build this "House of Millions of Years United with Thebes," as the Ramesseum was called in his day, lay on the edge of the desert between the temples of Kings Amunhotep II and Tuthmosis IV of Dynasty XVIII. Here he erected not only a temple, which reproduced elements of Karnak on a smaller scale, but also a palace, storerooms and housing for his funerary priests. The magazines or warehouses of the Ramesseum provide some idea of the size and complexity of this enterprise. The area of the enclosed temple precinct devoted to storage of commodities was three times that allotted to the temple itself. There were 20 large, vaulted, mudbrick granaries, each of which held sufficient barley and emmer wheat to feed 60 families for more than two years. Similarly, great amounts of other goods, like wine, honey and oil, filled smaller storerooms.

In the Ramesseum temple area proper, a massive stone pylon opened onto an open-air court flanked on the north and south by pillars and columns. Dominating this court and, indeed, the entire temple was a 66-foot-high, 1000-ton seated statue of Ramesses, with an inscription which, according to ancient Greek translators, proclaimed him the King of Kings. A stairway led to a second open-air colonnaded court where additional towering statues of the king, this time represented as Osiris, god of resurrection, flanked pillars on the east and west sides. From the second court, a 48-columned hypostyle hall, second in size only to Karnak's, led to three smaller columned halls and finally to a sanctuary in the rear.

Nowhere in Egypt are ancient storerooms better preserved than at the Ramesseum. The largest, which were granaries, were filled through holes in the roof and emptied through side doors.

The Ramesseum was oriented to the Luxor temple on the east bank of the Nile so that during the annual "Beautiful Feast of the Valley" celebrations (Cat. No. 56), the god Amun might travel in his royal barque across the river and visit Ramesses the Great's funerary temple. Here in the "House of Millions of Years," the dead king and the god would become one.

As one group of builders and artisans was constructing the Ramesseum, a second group worked on Ramesses the Great's tomb. Their task involved carving and decorating the tomb according to precise specifications so that the king's resurrection and rebirth would be assured. The Ramesseum was essentially completed by Year 20 based on the early spelling of the king's name which changed slightly from Thebes to Nubia after Year 20.

This select group of approximately 50 artisans and supervisors reported directly to the vizier. They lived in Deir el Medina, a village in Western Thebes founded in early Dynasty XVIII to provide convenient living quarters for royal tomb builders and their families. By the time of Ramesses II's rule, the village had grown considerably in size and prosperity. Inside a protective wall, about 70 houses were grouped in contiguous units along two main avenues. Gates at the north and south ends excluded those who did not belong. Around the village lay its temples, tombs and tomb chapels. Total population is estimated to have been around 300.

Excavators at Deir el Medina have uncovered a wealth of domestic and archival material as yet unsurpassed in amount and state of preservation. Remains from the village, including the "Journal of the Necropolis," a day-to-day account written on ostraca about the mundane trivialities of work at the tomb, provide a window to the inner workings of an ancient enterprise. Work schedules, equipment, delivery of sup-

Pillagers and an earthquake reduced the Ramesseum to a ruin. Although now only a shadow of its former magnificence, the statue to the right is one of the largest ever carved from a single block of stone.

Following page. The second court of the Ramesseum with statues of the King. His crossed arms holding crook and flail and mummiform body identify him as Osiris, god of resurrection.

Paint pigments were mixed with water and applied with a reed brush. The owner of this palette made the greatest use of blue and black.

One of the main streets at Deir e
Medina. Houses shared side walls.

Debris from repeated floods now
fills the burial chamber in the tom
of Ramesses the Great.

Servant figures called shawabtis
attended to the needs of the king in
the afterlife. From the tomb of
Ramesses II.

Upon reaching the square chamber or well, known as the "Hall of Waiting," the royal mummy halted briefly, perhaps for ritual purposes, before proceeding to the four-pillared "Chariot Hall," also called the "Hall of Repulsing Rebels." Here, the demons of the netherworld met their demise. The walls of the next two passages were inscribed with the familiar texts and rites used in the "Opening of the Mouth" ceremony which had to be accomplished before he entered the next chamber, the "Hall of Truth," if his resurrection and divinity were to be guaranteed. Finally, the king arrived in the "House of Gold," the vaulted burial chamber, decorated, like a ceiling in the Ramesseum, with astronomical scenes (Cat. No. 54). Thus, Ramesses the Great had completed his journey through the netherworld and, at the exact moment the sun rose on the eastern horizon of the sky the next day, he entered into blissful eternal life.

Offering bearers brought in Ramesses the Great's funerary equipment, and priests checked to make sure he had all the essentials he would need in the afterlife. As they departed, the last priest to leave swept away all footprints and closed the tomb for eternity. The broom, the remains of the funerary meal and the remnants of the embalming materials were interred beside the tomb, so that they would be available to the king in the netherworld.

Thus, the proper rituals having been observed, the new king, Merneptah, Ramesses the Great's thirteenth son, could take his place as god on earth. The transition of power was peaceful; chaos was averted; Egypt was safe. Once again *Ma'at* was restored.

Priests sealed the doors of the
tomb at the end of the burial
ceremony. From the tomb of
Sennedjem at Deir el Medina.

112

Aftermath: Desecration and Loss

Unfortunately all did not happen as Ramesses the Great intended.

Merneptah was in his sixties by the time he became king. Most likely he had gained experience assisting his father during the last decade or so of the aging monarch's life. For the next ten years, Merneptah continued Ramesses II's policies and attempted to maintain Egypt's glory. He erected temples and palaces, commissioned statues, exploited mineral resources and defended the empire against foreign incursions.

For reasons that remain shrouded in mystery, when Merneptah died, his legitimate son disappeared. Instead, Amunmesse, half brother of Merneptah and son of Ramesses II by a minor queen, seized power but ruled only briefly. In the 23 years following Merneptah's death, Egypt saw four different pharaohs. The last ruler of Dynasty XIX was Queen Tausert (Cat. No. 70), wife of King Sety II. Her demise, two years after she came to power, marked the end of Ramesses the Great's direct line. Nevertheless, an additional nine kings of the next dynasty bore his name.

Dynasty XX opened with the two-year reign of a king named Seth-nakht, whose parentage is unknown. His son, Ramesses III, ruled for 32 years, and as the namesake of Ramesses the Great, he made Ramesses II his mentor. Ramesses the Great's ideals became his. He named his children after those of Ramesses II's, and he modeled his funerary temple (Medinet Habu) after the Ramesseum. In spite of these valiant efforts by Ramesses III, accumulating problems began to rob Egypt of her former splendor. He was forced to defend Egypt's borders on three different occasions, and at home he battled a powerful priesthood, bureaucratic incompetence, workers' strikes and a palace plot to murder him.

Royal authority continued its rapid decline through the end of Dynasty XX, until, finally, low Niles, inflation and widespread corruption rendered the last Ramesside kings powerless. It was probably during this period of turmoil, some 100 or so years after Ramesses the Great had been laid to rest, that robbers first violated his tomb. They stole his golden coffins, ritual equipment, provisions for the afterlife and even the jewels on his mummy, leaving behind only his defiled, naked torso.

Fearing wholesale destruction of the necropolis and the consequences it might bring, officials in Western Thebes formed a commission to investigate. They reported that many tombs had, in fact, been plundered. What a furor that must have caused, especially since it involved the bribery of some prominent members of the community! As duly recorded on papyri now in the British Museum, select suspects were rounded up, tried and punished.

The problems continued, however. Several years later, the High Priest of Amun, Herihor, authorized his priesthood to gather the desecrated bodies of Egypt's New Kingdom kings, rewrap them and rebury them in safer hiding places. They adorned Ramesses the Great's mummy with new floral garlands and placed it in a plain wooden coffin which had been made originally for one of his predecessors (perhaps Horemheb or Ramesses I). They laid him to rest in the tomb of his father, Sety I, beside a number of his royal ancestors and descendants. It was the fifteenth day of the Third month of *Peret* in Year 24 of Ramesses XI (ca. 1075 B.C.), as priests recorded on his new coffin.

Still, the country continued to battle with internal problems, split by a priesthood

King of kings, Ozymandias.
Originally, 66 feet tall and 1,000
tons.

which had gained power in Upper Egypt while kings in the Delta ruled Lower Egypt from Tanis. The Age of the Ramessides had come to an end.

Over the next 100 years of rule by Dynasty XXI kings, the tomb robberies continued. When High Priest of Amun, Pinodjem II, died, his fellow priests took steps to end them. Once again, they gathered the royal bodies and used the activities surrounding Pinodjem's burial as a foil to hide all of Egypt's great New Kingdom kings, together with bodies of their own dead, in the narrow pit tomb of Queen Inhapy, which they had enlarged to accommodate the additions. They closed the tomb near Deir el Bahari, on the twentieth day of the Fourth month of *Peret* in Year 10 of King Siamun (ca. 969 B.C.). There, miraculously, for more than 2800 years, all the bodies, including that of Ramesses II, remained lost and forgotten.

Afterlife: Greatness Remembered

His body was desecrated, his tomb lost, but Ramesses the Great lived on. After the monuments of Pi-Ramesses were dismantled and moved to Tanis, the memory of Ramesses the Great traveled with them, and worship of Ramesses the god continued at the new sites and elsewhere. For the next 1000 years, people paid homage to his colossi and venerated him in his temples throughout the land. In the Ptolemaic Period (331-30 B.C.), his cult supported its own priesthood.

When Egypt became a vacationland for ancient Greek and Roman travelers and tourists, their accounts of their journeys, almost without fail, mentioned the still splendid monuments of Ramesses the Great. The Ramesseum, in particular, with its 1000-ton megalith statue excited awe. The chronicler, Diodorus of Sicily, writing about 60 B.C., noted the statue's unbelievable size and quality. Thorough journalist that he was, he provided a translation of the hieroglyphs inscribed on its base: "King of Kings am I, Ozymandias. If anyone would know how great I am...let him surpass one of my works." [32] Ozymandias is the Greek version of the throne name of Ramesses II, *User-Ma'at-Ra*.

The name stuck, and millennia later the English nineteenth century poet, Percy Bysshe Shelley, further immortalized the same statue in his well-known poem, "Ozymandias." By then, however, earthquakes and looting had reduced both the Ramesseum and its statue to a ruin, which Shelley described:

> "...Two vast and trunkless legs of stone
> Stand in the desert. Near them on the sand,
> Half sunk, a shatter'd visage lies...
> 'My name is Ozymandias, king of kings:
> Look on my works, ye Mighty, and despair!'
> Nothing beside remains. Round the decay
> Of that colossal wreck, boundless and bare,
> The lone and level sands stretch far away." [33]

Although despoiled, the Ramesseum was never lost to history. Such was not the case with Abu Simbel, Ramesses II's majestic monument to himself in Nubia, some 175 miles south of Aswan. We know it still dominated the landscape in Dynasty XXVI, when Greek mercenaries marching south carved their names on the leg of one of the colossi. But slowly, over the centuries, the drifting Nubian sands virtually covered this lofty temple.

Colossal statues of Ramesses the Great at Abu Simbel dominate the Nubian landscape once again.

Notes

Chapter I—Ramesses the King

[1] From the dedicatory inscription of Abydos, as translated by D.B. Redford, *Pharaonic King-Lists, Annals and Day Books: A Contribution to the Egyptian Sense of History* (Mississauga, 1986) 265-266.

[2] From Papyrus Anastasi IV, as translated by R. Caminos, *Late-Egyptian Miscellanies* (London, 1954) 150.

[3] From Papyrus Sallier IV, Caminos 334.

[4] From the Kadesh poem and bulletin adapted from R.O. Faulkner, "The Battle of Kadesh" *MDAIK* 16 (1958) 101, 104.

[5] Faulkner 104.

[6] Faulkner 104.

[7] From the abridged version of the first Hittite marriage stela, as translated by A.R. Schulman, "Diplomatic Marriage in the Egyptian New Kingdom," *JNES* 38 (1979) 186, note 41.

[8] Schulman 186.

Chapter II—Egypt in the Ramesside Age

[9] From the "Blessings of Ptah" at Abu Simbel, adapted from J.H. Breasted, *Ancient Records of Egypt III* (Chicago, 1906) 81.

[10] As translated by M. Abd el-Razik, "The Dedicatory and Building Texts of Ramesses II in Luxor Temple II: Interpretation," *JEA* 61 (1975):125.

[11] As translated by D.B. Redford, "The Earliest Years of Ramesses II, and the Building of the Ramesside Court at Luxor," *JEA* 57 (1971):114.

[12] Redford 114.

[13] From a stela of Sety I from Aswan, Breasted 88.

[14] From the Manshiyet es-Sadr stela, Redford 112.

[15] From the Manshiyet es-Sadr stela, as translated by E. Uphill, "Pithom and Raamses," *JNES* 28 (1969):33.

[16] Uphill 33.

[17] From an inscription on the Luxor temple, Redford 114.

[18] From the Manshiyet es-Sadr stela, as translated by A. Hamada, "Stela from Manshiyet es-Sadr," *ASAE* 38 (1938):228.

[19] From the Quban stela, Breasted 120-121.

[20] Breasted 120-121.

[21] From Papyrus Anastasi IV, Caminos 169.

[22] Caminos 169.

[23] Caminos 169.

[24] Caminos 169.

[25] From Papyrus Anastasi V, Caminos 273-274.

[26] From Papyrus Anastasi V, Caminos 247.

[27] From Papyrus Lansing, Caminos 412-413.

[28] Caminos 412-413.

[29] From Papyrus Anastasi III, Caminos 83.

[30] From Papyrus Anastasi II, Caminos 51.

[31] From Papyrus Anastasi V, Caminos 247.

Chapter III—Quest for Immortality

[32] *Diodorus of Sicily I*, trans. C.H. Oldfather (Cambridge, 1968) 169. Diodorus was citing the third century B.C. historian Hecataeus of Abdera.

[33] Percy Bysshe Shelley, "Ozymandias," from *The New Oxford Book of English Verse*, ed. Helen Gardner (New York and Oxford, 1972) 580.

Ramesses II's thirteenth son, Merneptah, assumed the throne upon his father's death. From Thebes.

Scale Representations of Objects in the Exhibition

Scale: 1 inch = 1 foot

13

14

15

16

17

18

19

20

21

22

23

24

25

26

27

28

29

30

31

32

33

34

35

36

37

38

39

42

40

44

41

45

47

43

48

49

46

50

51, 52

53

55

54

56

57

58

59

62

63

69

70

64

65

66

67

68

71

72

131

2
Meryetamun, Daughter and Wife of Ramesses II

An artistic masterwork of the Nineteenth Dynasty, this royal female statue, discovered in 1896, was long thought to represent Meryetamun, but proof was not forthcoming until just a few years ago. Workers excavated a trench prior to building a school in the upper Egyptian city of Akhmim in 1981. They discovered a colossal statue strikingly similar to the present example in physiognomy, dress, accoutrements, and cultic titles. Inscribed on the back of the Akhmim statue was the name of its owner, Meryetamun, daughter and later wife of Ramesses the Great. Undoubtedly, it is she who is represented here as well. Her soft round face, slightly protruding eyes highlighted by incised lines, and full sensuous lips characterize the best of Ramesside art.

Meryetamun wears a crown of uraeii and sun disks known as a *modius*. Two additional uraeii attached with a band to the front of her long, ornately curled wig wear the crowns of Upper and Lower Egypt and further indicate her royal status. Ball earrings, a broad collar largely made up of beads in the shape of *nefer* signs (the hieroglyphic word for beauty), and a wide bracelet adorn her. In her left hand she clutches a *menat* (ceremonial necklace and counterweight) bearing the head of Hathor attached to strings of beads.

Hathor was the goddess of love, music and dance, and *menats* were frequently carried by women who served as her priestesses, as Meryetamun was. The hieroglyphic inscription on her back further relates that she was Sistrum Player for the Goddess Mut (associated with Hathor) and Dancer for the God Horus. Just as the king officiated as high priest, so too did royal wives have a role in Egyptian religious practices.

Material: Limestone
Provenance: Thebes, northwest of the Ramesseum
Height: 75 cm. (29.5 in.)
Width: 44 cm. (17.3 in.)
Date: New Kingdom, Dynasty XIX, Ramesses II
Cairo Accession No.: JE 31413 = CG 600
Catalogue References:
Brigham Young University No. 66
Montreal and Vancouver No. 28

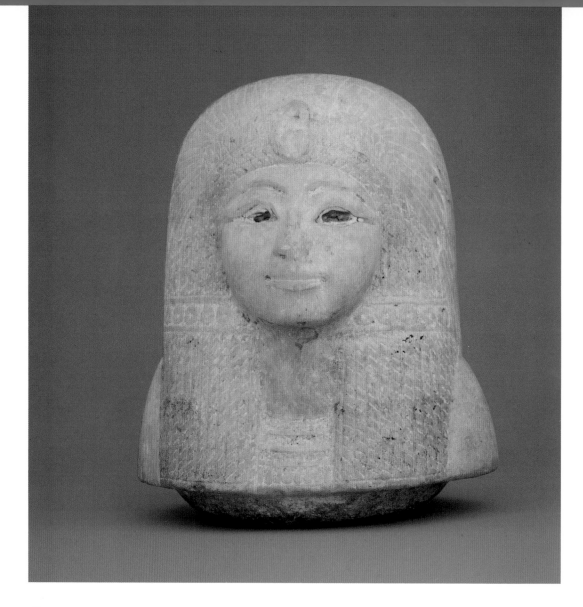

3
Canopic Lid of Queen Tuya, Mother of Ramesses II

Females carried the royal blood line in ancient Egypt, and every New Kingdom king regarded himself as the off-spring of his earthly mother and heavenly father Amun. Accordingly, queens, and especially queen mothers, enjoyed special reverence. Queen Tuya, Great Royal Wife of Sety I and mother of Ramesses II, was honored by both husband and son with statues, temples, and a tomb. She lived until at least the twenty-second year of her son's rule.

Queen Tuya's likeness forms the lid of one of four canopic jars from her tomb. Inside these jars were her internal organs, removed from her body at the time of mummification and spe-cially treated. In 1972, a joint Egyptian-French expedition discovered Tuya's tomb in the Valley of the Queens.

Idealizing rather than portrait-like, the queen's face smiles sweetly from beneath a heavy, curled wig. A vul-ture cap, atop the wig, sym-bolizes her royal status. The eyes were once inlaid, probably with glass.

Material: Alabaster
Provenance: Thebes, Valley of the Queens, tomb of Queen Tuya (No. 80)
Height: 17 cm. (6.7 in.)
Diam. of head: 15 cm. (5.9 in.)
Date: New Kingdom, Dynasty XIX, Ramesses II
Luxor Museum Entry No.: J 191
Catalogue References:
Brigham Young University No. 56
Montreal and Vancouver No. 5

4
King Ramesses II

Only the upper part of this royal statue is preserved, and the fragmentary inscription on the back pillar does not include the owner's name. However, the distinctive style leaves little doubt that it represents Ramesses the Great. His round face, high cheekbones, slightly bulging almond-shaped eyes, and sweet smiling mouth are reminiscent of other statues of the king and his family members (Cat. Nos. 2, 3, 5, 6, 71 and 72). It shares a timeless, forever youthful quality with some of the best Ramesside statuary.

Ramesses II wears a short curled wig with a central uraeus attached by means of a band tied at the back and terminating at each side in another uraeus. His torso is clothed in a finely pleated linen garment knotted just below the right breast, a beaded broad collar, and a bracelet shaped like an *udjat* eye. Combining a human eye with the facial markings of the falcon god Horus, the *udjat* symbolized health and prosperity. The outline of a *heka* scepter, a shepherd's crook which represented kingship, may still be seen in the king's right hand. The torso's slightly forward angle suggests that it originally came from a seated statue.

Material: Granite
Provenance: Tanis
Height: 82.5 cm. (32.5 in.)
Width: 64 cm. (25.2 in.)
Date: New Kingdom, Dynasty XIX, Ramesses II
Cairo Accession No.: CG 616
Catalogue References:
   Brigham Young University No. 54
   Montreal and Vancouver No. 67

5
Ramesses II Making an Offering

On a base covered with the incised leaves of the *ished* tree, Ramesses II, outstretched, presents an altar-shaped box to his god. At the front, food offerings cover a mat.

The *ished*, or persea tree, grew in the temple courtyard of the sacred city of Heliopolis since the beginning of time. On every coronation day the king's titulary was proclaimed throughout the land. The goddess of writing, Seshat, or her delegate inscribed the name

on the leaves of the *ished*. This assured the king a long and prosperous rule. Here the name inscribed on the leaves is *User-Ma'at-Ra*, Ramesses II's coronation name. Probably this statue was either made at the time of the coronation or later in commemoration of it. The text around the statue's base promises that "his (Ramesses II's) achievements are confirmed hundreds of thousands of times on the leaves of the sacred *ished* tree."

Ramesses II wears the *nemes*, a headcloth reserved for kings, and a uraeus emerges from his brow. Around his waist, a decorated belt holds a finely pleated linen kilt in place. His downcast eyes and reverent expression complement his prostrate stance.

This statue was one of almost a thousand stone sculptures (Cat. Nos. 6, 7, 12 and 54) deposited in a fourteen meter-deep pit in front of the Seventh Pylon

in the temple of Karnak (Karnak cachette) during a "housecleaning" effort of the early Ptolemaic Era (ca. 300-250 B.C.).

Material: Schist
Provenance: Thebes, Karnak
Height: 27.5 cm. (10.8 in.)
Maximum width (base): 75.8 cm. (29.8 in.)
Length (without restoration): 12.5 cm. (4.9 in.)
Date: New Kingdom, Dynasty XIX, Ramesses II
Cairo Accession No.: JE 37423 = CG 42142
Catalogue References:
 Brigham Young University No. 20
 Montreal and Vancouver No. 64

6
Ramesses the Great as a Sphinx

Noted for his strength and power, the lion symbolized kingship in ancient Egypt. As early as the Old Kingdom (ca. 2700-2200 B.C.), Egyptian artisans combined the head of the reigning monarch with the body of the king of beasts to create an awesome image.

Here, a rather idealized, reverential representation of the head of Ramesses II joins a taut, powerful leonine body. The *nemes* headcloth and broad collar help mask the transition between anthropomorphic and zoo-morphic forms.

The human-handed sphinx statue type began only in the New Kingdom (ca. 1550 B.C.). Here the hands clasp a high-shouldered vase surmounted by a ram's head. The ram was sacred to the god Amun (Cat. No. 53). Pharaoh tradi-tionally offered a vessel of this type to Amun on the Egyptian New Year (mid-July). This coincided with rising floodwaters at Aswan, which brought with them renewed fertility for the land. Accordingly, an actual vessel of this shape, often made of precious metal, contained the first flood waters. It might also hold sacred unguents for pre-sentation to the gods in return for a long and pros-perous life.

Inscribed on the front of the vessel are Ramesses II's birth name and coronation name. Like Cat. Nos. 5, 7, 12 and 54, it was found in the cachette of statues at Karnak.

Material: Sandstone
Provenance: Thebes, Karnak
Height: 18 cm. (7.1 in.)
Length: 37 cm. (14.6 in.)
Width: 9 cm. (3.5 in.)
Date: New Kingdom, Dynasty XIX, Ramesses II
Cairo Accession No.: CG 38060 = CG 42146
Catalogue References:
  Brigham Young University No. 19
  Montreal and Vancouver No. 65

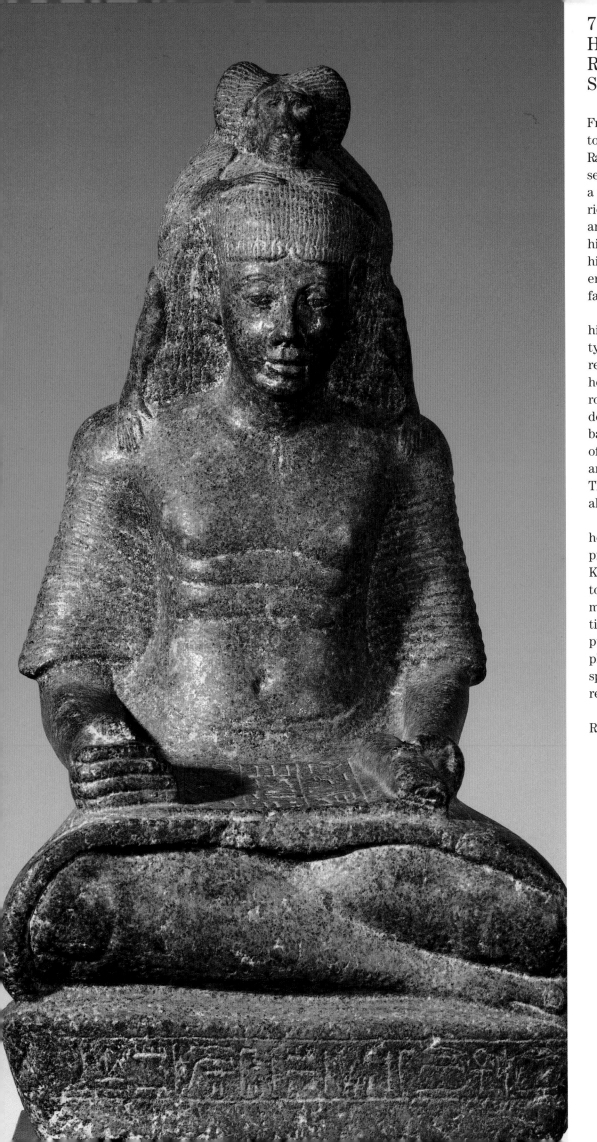

7

High Priest of Amun, Ramesses-nakht as a Scribe

From the reign of Ramesses IV to at least Year Two of Ramesses IX, Ramesses-nakht served as priest of Amun, a powerful office which carried with it both religious and political power. When his son Nesamun succeeded him in this position, he erected this statue in his father's honor.

Ramesses-nakht sits with his legs crossed under him, a typical scribal pose and a reference to another office he held. The papyrus unrolled on his lap provides details about his life. The baboon embracing his head, offering him both protection and counsel, represents Thoth, god of scribes and of all written things.

Although the high priesthood was certainly the more prestigious position, New Kingdom literary texts refer to the scribal office as the most desirable of all occupations a young Egyptian might pursue. It brought with it pleasant working conditions, special privileges, and the respect of all.

The garment worn by Ramesses-nakht consists of

wo elements, both made of
ine linen probably pleated by
1and. A bag tunic slipped
over his head and knotted at
he neck covers his chest. A
separate piece of material
wrapped around his waist
forms the skirt. The rolls of
at on his torso and his
ample stomach indicate that
1e chose to be represented in
corpulent prosperity. A deli-
cately curled, shoulder-length
wig frames his reverent gaze.

Like Cat. Nos. 5, 6, 7 and
54, this statue was part of
he Karnak cachette.

Material: Granite
Provenance: Thebes, Karnak
Height: 75 cm. (29.5 in.)
Width: 43 cm. (16.9 in.)
Depth: 39 cm. (15.4 in.)
Date: New Kingdom, Dynasty XX,
   Ramesses IV-Ramesses IX
Cairo Accession No.: JE 36582 =
   CG 42162
Catalogue References:
   Brigham Young University No. 4
   Montreal and Vancouver No. 7

8
Scribal Palette

Part of the equipment essential to every scribe (Cat. No.
12) was a palette. In the
New Kingdom, the palette
was generally rectangular
and had depressions on one
end for cakes of black and
red ink, as well as a central
slot to hold fine reed pens.
Scribes used black ink, made
from carbon mixed with
water to make it flow and
gum to make it adhere, for
the text's main body and also
to outline any figural decoration. They inscribed important passages and headings
in red ink made from ochre
similarly mixed with water
and gum. Egyptian scribes
wrote on papyrus (Cat. No.
23), limestone ostraca (Cat.
Nos. 53 and 57) and wooden
tablets, in addition to temples,
tombs, and statuary.

The well-equipped scribe
would also have owned a
mortar and pestle for grinding pigments, a knife for
trimming or cutting papyrus,
and a burnishing stone for
smoothing rough surfaces.

Not only scribes, but every
man needed a palette in the
afterlife to gain access to the
secrets of the god of writing,
Thoth (Cat. No. 7), thereby
avoiding all the horrible pitfalls of the netherworld.
Because the pen slot on this
palette is only indicated
rather than carved out, it is
certain that it was made to
be part of the burial equipment and not intended for
daily use. A *shen* sign,
the hieroglyph meaning "to
protect and enclose" (Cat.
Nos. 42 and 72) surrounds
each ink depression.

Material: Schist
Provenance: Tell el Ruba'a
Length: 32.3 cm. (12.7 in.)
Width: 6 cm. (2.4 in.)
Date: Late Period
Cairo Accession No.: Special
   Register 305 = CG 69033
Catalogue References:
   Brigham Young University No. 2
   Montreal and Vancouver No. 9

Sennedjem's Right Angle and Plumb Level

To ensure that all building surfaces were smooth and perfectly aligned, ancient Egyptian architects and craftsmen employed a right angle and plumb level, both of which remain essential instruments of the carpenter's trade today.

Three slats of wood join in an A-shape to form the right angle, and a limestone bob is suspended by a cord from the top. When placed against a perfectly flat surface, the string of the bob would fall between the two lines incised in the middle of the crosspiece. If the surface were not properly aligned, the bob would then indicate the necessary corrections.

The plumb level, consisting of two short pieces of wood projecting at right angles from a longer slab, operated on a similar principle. A string with attached bob was threaded out the top of the long slab and uppermost short projection. The string would just touch the lowermost projection when the long slab was held against an even, vertical surface.

These tools, like the cubit rod (Cat. No. 11), belonged to the Servant in the Place of Truth Sennedjem who included them in his tomb (together with Cat. Nos. 11, 35, 37, 41, 42, 43, 44 and 45). In the inscription on the right angle, he asks the god Ptah

to ensure him a good burial after attaining a venerable age, and he requests the composite god Ra-Horakhty-Atum to make him a luminous spirit in the sky and a powerful man on earth. The plumb level is inscribed only with his name and another title, Servant of the Master of the Two Lands (i.e. the king).

9
Material: Wood and limestone
Provenance: Thebes, Deir el
    Medina, Tomb of Sennedjem
    (T.T.1)
Length of Diagonal: 36.3 cm.
    (14.3 in.)
Length of Horizontal: 22.2 cm.
    (8.7 in.)
Height of Bob: 5.3 cm. (2.1 in.)
Date: New Kingdom, Dynasty XIX,
    Sety I-Ramesses II
Cairo Accession No.: JE 27258
Catalogue References:
    Brigham Young University No. 35
    Montreal and Vancouver No. 37

10
Material: Wood and limestone
Provenance: Thebes, Deir el
    Medina, Tomb of Sennedjem
    (T.T.1)
Height of Level: 48.6 cm. (19.1 in.)
Height of Bob: 5 cm. (1.96 in.)
Date: New Kingdom, Dynasty XIX,
    Sety I-Ramesses II
Cairo Accession No.: JE 27260
Catalogue References:
    Brigham Young University No. 37
    Montreal and Vancouver No. 38

10

9

11
Sennedjem's
Cubit Rod

To calculate land area and to build temples, tombs, and State buildings, the ancient Egyptians used a standard unit of measure known as the royal cubit. Sculpture and relief were also constructed with the aid of a cubit measure, but a slightly smaller cubit was used.

The length of the royal cubit (20.6 inches or 52.5 centimeters) and its subdivisions were based on human body measurements and ratios. One royal cubit represented the distance from the elbow to the tip of the longest finger. It also equaled seven times the width of the palm and twenty-eight finger widths. All these units are marked off on the cubit rod shown here, which belonged to the artisan and Servant in the Place of Truth Sennedjem (Cat. Nos. 9, 10, 35, 37, 41, 42, 43, 44 and 45).

Sennedjem may have used this cubit rod to help build and decorate the tombs of Sety I and Ramesses II in the Valley of the Kings, as well as his own splendid burial place. Although Sennedjem lived, worked, and was buried at Deir el Medina, he, like the architect May (Cat. No. 12), sought the favor of the Memphite god and patron of craftsmen, Ptah, who was revered throughout Egypt.

Material: Wood
Provenance: Thebes, Deir el Medina, Tomb of Sennedjem (T.T.1)
Length: 52.7 cm. (20.7 in.)
Date: New Kingdom, Dynasty XIX, Sety I-Ramesses II
Cairo Accession No.: JE 27211
Catalogue Reference: Brigham Young University No. 35

The Architect May

Ramesses the Great commissioned temples and State buildings from the Delta in the North to as far South as Nubia, justly earning his reputation as one of the most prolific builders of all time. The responsibility for executing these myriad building projects fell to his trusted officials. A key person was the chief architect May, shown here in a seated position with his palms upturned in reverence.

Son of the Chief of Works Bakenamun, May followed in his father's footsteps. In his long career, he served not only Ramesses II but also his successor Merneptah, whose cartouches are inscribed on May's shoulders. The statue was found in Memphis near the temple of Merneptah during a clandestine excavation. In 1937 it was recovered for the Cairo Museum.

The majority of the standing monuments in ancient Memphis bear the name of Ramesses II, and May may well have been responsible for erecting them. In the inscription incised on his long wrap-around skirt, he first invokes Ptah, the god of Memphis and patron of craftsmen, asking for life, prosperity, and health. May's jurisdiction extended to other major cities of Ramesses II as well, including Heliopolis, Thebes, and Pi-Ramesses, where he built temples to Ra and Amun as well as to Ptah. He also held military titles. Not only the actual building, but also the obtaining of suitable building materials seems to have been his responsibility. Travelling as far south as Aswan to quarry granite, he recorded his presence in the form of an inscription on the cliff face of the nearby island of Sehel.

A wavy, shoulder-length wig frames May's stern, round face. Somewhat heavier than the ideal body of Egyptian youth, his torso is marked by swollen breasts and fleshy folds, signs of prosperity that come with age. His image evokes dignity, wisdom, and serenity.

Material: Granite
Provenance: Memphis
Height: 74 cm. (29.1 in.)
Base Width: 38.5 cm. (15.2 in.)
Base Depth: 47.3 cm. (18.6 in.)
Date: New Kingdom, Dynasty XIX,
    Ramesses II-Merneptah
Cairo Accession No.: JE 67878
Catalogue References:
    Brigham Young University No. 38
    Montreal and Vancouver No. 6

13
Dignitaries in Procession

High officials of the court hurry forward eagerly, perhaps to attend a ceremony connected with a presentation of the Gold of Valor necklaces shown at the far left and in Cat. No. 65. The reliefs come from an as yet unidentified private tomb in Western Thebes. The style of the carving, the profiles of the figures, and their garments bear the unmistakable stamp of a Ramesside Period artisan.

Set apart on each block by virtue of their spacing and their distinctive clothing are the viziers of the North and South, key officials of the king whose responsibility it was to coordinate the internal affairs of their respective regions (Cat. No. 14). They wear the vizier's traditional long, sheath-like garment held in place by narrow shoulder straps. The first vizier on the left block below

holds the crook and a single-plumed ceremonial fan. The former was a symbol of rulership, and the latter was a badge of honor frequently carried by high dignitaries. Officials of lesser significance are represented *en masse* behind the viziers. Wearing identical shoulder-length wigs and long, billowy garments, they carry papyrus rolls and walking sticks. The fact that all the officials are barefoot suggests that they were in the company of the king. Ancient Egyptian custom dictated the removal of one's sandals in the presence of superiors.

Material: Sandstone
Provenance: Thebes, Asasif
Maximum Height: 102 cm.
  (40.2 in.)
Maximum Width: 117 cm. (46.1 in.)
Date: New Kingdom, Dynasty XIX
Cairo Museum Temporary Register
  No.: 14/6/24/20 = Special
  Register No. 11775
Catalogue References:
  Brigham Young University No. 9
  Montreal and Vancouver No. 10

14
The Vizier Khay

Under the king, the highest government officials were two viziers. One administered internal affairs in Lower Egypt (North) and the other had jurisdiction over Upper Egypt (South). Khay, shown here, served Ramesses the Great as Vizier of the South for about sixteen years, beginning in approximately the thirtieth year of Ramesses II's rule. One of his responsibilities was to arrange jubilee festivals for the king (celebrations of the king's rejuvenation), and he left a record of this important task in the form of rock-cut stelae at the Gebel Silsileh sandstone quarries, some 65 kilometers north of Aswan, where he is shown offering a votive statue to the local goddess Anukis. According to the inscription on the statue in the exhibition, Khay's career also included service to Ramesses II in the capacity of steward and high priest of the goddess of Truth (Maat).

Khay is shown in a squatting position, and his body has been abstracted into a cubic form called a "block statue." A type known since early Dynasty XII (approximately 2000 B.C.), it was intended primarily as a temple statue. Here, it incorporates the facade of a naos (shrine) into which are sculpted the chief god of Thebes, Amun, and his consort, Mut. Khay's block statue probably sat in the temple of Karnak for about 1,000 years until it, together with close to one thousand other statues, was deposited in a pit outside the Seventh Pylon at Karnak (Cat. Nos. 5, 6, 7 and 12).

In contrast to the relative plainness of his body, Khay's head shows careful detail. His layered, precisely curled wig, pierced ears, heavy face, high cheekbones, slightly bulging eyes, thin nose, wide nostrils, and fleshy lips are characteristic of some of the finer statuary of the Ramesside Period.

Material: Granite
Provenance: Thebes, Karnak
Height: 73 cm. (28.7 in.)
Date: New Kingdom, Dynasty XIX, Ramesses II
Cairo Accession No.: JE 37406 = CG 42165
Catalogue References: Brigham Young University No. 8 Montreal and Vancouver— (unnumbered)

15
Headrest

Representations of headrests in use show that the Egyptians slept on their sides so their cheeks and upper necks rested in the U-shaped area. Perhaps employed more for their protective and rejuvenative connotations than for comfort, headrests were found both in houses and tombs. The semicircular concave shape on a support approximated the hieroglyph for horizon (𓈌). With the spherical shape of the head placed in the middle, it brought to mind the image of the morning sun rising between two mountain peaks. Just as the sun was reborn at the start of a new day, so too did the Egyptians hope to survive the dangers of the night and the netherworld and awake rejuvenated, daily and eternally.

The scene carved on the front of the columnar support reinforces the image of protection. Bes, the leonine dwarf god holding knives in both forepaws and hindlegs, leans on the hieroglyph for protection. A snake spews from his mouth. Bes guarded the household and protected women in childbirth. By virtue of his ferocious appearance, and in this example with the knives he holds, he frightened away or destroyed malevolent spirits just as he consumed the writhing serpent. In a similar manner he was thought to guard sleeping souls.

A funerary offering formula incised on the base indicates that this headrest was intended for use in the tomb.

Material: Wood
Provenance: Thebes, Gurna
Height: 20 cm. (7.9 in.)
Width: 14 cm. (5.5 in.)
Length: 36 cm. (14.2 in.)
Date: New Kingdom, Dynasty
  XVIII
Cairo Accession No.: JE 6269
Catalogue References:
  Brigham Young University No. 40
  Montreal and Vancouver No. 40

Swimming Girl

A young girl gracefully extended in the attitude of a swimmer once held a container in her out-stretched hands. Judging from similar pieces, the missing container may have taken the form of a duck, gazelle, or fish. The girl is nude except for a few articles of gold-foil jewelry seductively draped over her wood torso. These include bracelets, a broad collar, and bands across her chest. At one time a thin girdle encircled her hips. She wears a short, bobbed wig with a lock of longer hair gathered at the side, a hairstyle common to young girls.

The "swimming girl" belongs to a category of objects not fully understood. Clearly, she projects adolescent vitality. Most likely, the missing container once held a magical unguent whose youth-renewing properties would have been as effective in this world as in the afterlife.

Material: Wood
Provenance: Not known
Length: 34.5 cm. (13.6 in.)
Date: New Kingdom, Dynasty
 XVIII
Cairo Accession No.: JE 5218 =
 CG 45118
Catalogue References:
 Brigham Young University No. 70
 Montreal and Vancouver No. 60

17
Mirror

When polished, this bronze mirror would reflect an image almost as well as its modern counterpart. Like so many other objects, mirrors were both used in daily life and served a symbolic function in the afterlife.

The mirror consists of a slightly flattened disk with projecting tang riveted to a decorative handle. The circular shape was associated with the sun and its life-giving and life-renewing properties. The young servant girl whose nude, columnar body serves as the mirror's handle further emphasizes this fertility aspect. From her head emerges a papyrus umbel.

Other figural mirror handles of New Kingdom date feature the head of Hathor, goddess of love, music, joy, and inebriation or Bes, the protector of the household and of women in childbirth (Cat. No. 15). Most common, however, was the stem and umbel of the papyrus flower.

When not in use, the mirror would have been stored either in its own case or with other cosmetic articles in a chest. The Egyptian words for mirror were ''see-face'' and ''life.''

Material: Bronze
Provenance: Saqqara
Height: 30.5 cm. (12 in.)
Date: New Kingdom, Dynasty
  XVIII
Cairo Accession No.: JE 10888 =
  CG 44044
Catalogue References:
  Brigham Young University No. 65
  Montreal and Vancouver No. 53

18
Comb

Fairly sturdy combs like the present example groomed the thick, often greased hair of Egyptian wigs. This basic form commonly appeared in the New Kingdom. The vertical shape of the teeth is echoed in the incised lotus petals on the handle. Originally, a blue paste filled the space between the petals. Combs were frequently found with other cosmetic articles in houses and tombs.

Material: Wood
Provenance: Abusir el Melek
Height: 5 cm. (1.97 in.)
Length: 17 cm. (6.7 in.)
Date: New Kingdom, Dynasty XVIII
Cairo Accession No.: JE 36233 = CG 44316
Catalogue References:
    Brigham Young University No. 68
    Montreal and Vancouver No. 55

Razor

Both for cleanliness and for relief from the heat, Egyptian men and women kept their hair short and wore wigs for festive occasions. Except in rare instances, men were clean-shaven. Flint knives, readily available and cheap, probably served as razors for most. Those who could afford it would have used a bronze cutting implement like the one shown here. Its broad end forms the cutting edge; the wooden projection is the handle. Oil may have been used as a lubricant to make facial shaving less painful. Some barbers served as part of the regular staff of the palace, large estates, and the army. Others travelled from village to village, cutting hair in exchange for food or other commodities.

This razor probably belonged to a woman, one of two buried in the Deir el Medina tomb in which it was found.

Material: Bronze and wood
Provenance: Thebes, Deir el
  Medina (Tomb No. 1388)
Length: 16.6 cm. (6.5 in.)
Date: New Kingdom, Dynasty
  XVIII
Cairo Accession No.: JE 63686
Catalogue References:
  Brigham Young University No. 41
  Montreal and Vancouver No. 54

20, 21, 22
Kohl Containers

Both to highlight their eyes
and to protect them from the
sun's bright glare, Egyptian
men and women alike out-
lined their eyes with kohl.
Most commonly made from
galena, a naturally occuring
lead ore, kohl was ground to
a powder and stored in
decorative pots and tubes.
The cosmetic was applied
with a short stick. Three
faience examples are shown
here. (Faience is a powdered
mixture of mainly silica
which was fired at a high
temperature.) Kohl con-
tainers might also be made of
stone, bone, ivory, glass, pottery, wood, or reed.

Using pots to store kohl
dates back to the Old
Kingdom (ca. 2700-2200 B.C.).
Since the body shape and
color brought to mind the
blue lotus flower, artisans
added its pointed petals in
black glaze. A faience disk
with a tiny projection on the
underside to hold it in place
serves as the lid. Inside is a
cylindrical hollow.

Kohl tubes came into vogue
only in the New Kingdom.
The earliest were simple
hollow reeds. Then the shape
was copied in more perma-
nent materials which were
often fancifully decorated,
as these are. In one example,
a squatting monkey clutches
a kohl tube as if it were a
tree trunk. Since their
playful actions often
mimicked human ones,
monkeys afforded great
amusement, and they may
have been kept as household
pets. Frequently, in the New
Kingdom they appear as
decorative motifs. Two holes
near the top of the tube
were intended to secure
the lid. Monkey and tube

20

were made in one piece from a mold.

The appearance of two reeds bound together is imitated in the double faience tubes, and the vegetation motif continues through into the decoration. One tube undoubtedly held galena; the second may have contained eye paint of another color or a medicinal substance for the cure of eye diseases. A tiny hole between the two tubes once held the applicator. A nude servant girl holding a duck and a lotus bud decorates one side. On the reverse, a similar maiden holds a lotus flower aloft in each hand.

20
Material: Faience
Provenance: Abydos
Height: 4.7 cm. (1.9 in.)
Width: 3.8 cm. (1.5 in.)
Date: Second Intermediate Period
Cairo Accession No.: JE 30776 = CG 3681
Catalogue References:
  Brigham Young University No. 59
  Montreal and Vancouver No. 61

21
Material: Faience
Provenance: Kaw (?)
Height: 5 cm. (1.97 in.)
Date: New Kingdom, Dynasty XVIII
Cairo Accession No.: JE 31244 = CG 3979
Catalogue References:
  Brigham Young University No. 57
  Montreal and Vancouver No. 62

22
Material: Faience
Provenance: Abydos
Height: 13 cm. (5.1 in.)
Date: New Kingdom, Dynasty XVIII
Cairo Accession No.: JE 72178 = CG 3978
Catalogue References:
  Brigham Young University No. 58
  Montreal and Vancouver No. 63

21

22

23
Satirical Papyrus

Judging from their rich artistic and literary tradition, not only did Egyptians enjoy life, but also they poked fun at it. This papyrus reveals a complete reversal of roles. Animals act in a human capacity, and natural predators become servants to their prey. Here, cats attend mice, and foxes meekly perform menial tasks for a cow. The artist skillfully outlined the design in black and red and painted it with a pastel, almost impressionistic palette. The main figure seems to be a large mouse elegantly dressed and coiffed, seated on the traditional Egyptian birthing stool. A cat in front of her has just handed the mouse a chalice, while behind her a cat hairdresser arranges her wig. A nurse cat tenderly carrying the swaddled baby mouse and a cat with a large fan and a jug follow in procession. Walking in the other direction and totally oblivious to what is happening beside him, a fox carries a jar on a shoulder pole as another pours from a second jug into a basin. Beside it their cow mistress looks on.

Unique in its content but not in its nature, this papyrus belongs to a group of appealing genre scenes, most from the late Ramesside Period, which reflect a topsy-turvy world. Perhaps this forecasted the confusing political situation which heralded the end of the New Kingdom.

Material: Papyrus
Provenance: Not known
Height: 13 cm. (5.1 in.)
Total Length: 55.5 cm. (21.9 in.)
Date: New Kingdom, probably
    Dynasty XX
Cairo Accession No.: JE 31199
Catalogue References:
    Brigham Young University No. 3
    Montreal and Vancouver No. 15

24
Senet Game

Since the beginning of their recorded history (ca. 3200 B.C.), the Egyptians displayed a fondness for board games. They played them both for personal amusement and for their religious significance. Of all the board games, senet, shown here, achieved the greatest popularity.

Two opponents played the game, and each had his own distinctive playing pieces (between five and ten per player). The object was to move those pieces across the thirty squares (three rows of ten) of the game board. The throw of a knucklebone or the tossing of a set of throwsticks determined the number of squares moved. It was considered fortunate to land on some squares, while others brought bad luck, such as being forced to return to the start. The first player to move all his pieces off the board won the game.

Especially during the Ramesside Era, playing senet was rich in symbolism. One played not with an earthly partner but against Fate himself, and moving one's pieces across the game board was synonymous with traversing the pitfalls of the netherworld. Eternal life was the prize for victory. Both Sennedjem and Khonsu are shown playing senet against an invisible other-worldly opponent on their tomb door (Cat. No. 35) and sarcophagus (Cat. No. 36) respectively.

The drawer inside this ebony and ivory inlaid board stored the playing pieces. A sphinx and an ibex nibbling from the tree of life decorate the side panels.

Material: Box: Bone and ebony
  Game Pieces: Faience
Provenance: Thebes, Dra Abu'l
  Naga
Length: 26 cm. (10.2 in.)
Width: 7.6 cm. (2.99 in.)
Height: 4.7 cm. (1.9 in.)
Date: Second Intermediate Period,
  Dynasty XVII
Cairo Accession No.: JE 21462
Catalogue References:
  Brigham Young University No. 52
  Montreal and Vancouver No. 46

Shall...
varie...
mate...
as re...
ungu...
show...
inco...
anim...
there...
grace...
a duc...
dle o...
alaba...
prese...
to th...
gods,...
head...
dish i...
fresh...
a nat...
mix a...
Pred...
3,200...
The...

28

27

25
Miniature Chest

Jewelry, amulets, cosmetic substances, edibles, and articles whose true significance is lost to us were stored in miniature chests like this example. Made of contrasting colors of wood pegged together and inlaid with bone or ivory, it demonstrates the skill of the Egyptian cabinetmaker even on a small scale. Like many other boxes (Cat. Nos. 39 and 40), it closed by wrapping a cord alternately around knobs on the lid and body. A lump of wet clay sealed the chest.

The sloping lid and projecting cornice approximate the appearance of the symbolic palace of the South, a shape seen on a much larger scale in Khonsu's sarcophagus (Cat. No. 36). The Northern palace, characterized by a vaulted roof and vertical extensions of the side walls, is represented in Khabekhnet's shawabti box (Cat. No. 39).

Material: Wood and bone or ivory
Provenance: Thebes
Height: 7.8 cm. (3.1 in.)
Date: New Kingdom
Cairo Accession No.: JE 3318
Catalogue References:
  Brigham Young University No. 60
  Montreal and Vancouver No. 56

30, 31, 32, 33
Tiles from the
Royal Palace

Although the use of glazed ceramic tiles in Egyptian architectural decoration predates the Giza pyramids, no king made more lavish use of them than Ramesses the Great in his palace at Pi-Ramesses. Floors, parts of walls, doorways, windows, and throne daises came alive with color and life. The genre themes represented here probably came from the personal living quarters of the king and his family. More formal and awesome subjects, such as bound captives or heraldic lions, adorned the audience chamber and throne.

The zigzag background of the duck and fish tiles represents water. These may have formed part of a rectangular pool teeming with aquatic life and bordered by low flowering shrubs similar to those represented in Egyptian gardens. In the palace these tiles would have covered a floor, perhaps in one of the rooms of the harem. The sprightly, high-stepping pintail duck with his near impressionistic plummage represents a type of fowl as common today along the Nile as it must have been in the Ramesside Age. Not only was the duck an omnipresent decorative motif in Egyptian art, but also, strangled or trussed, it was a frequent funerary offering or gift to a deity. The fatter of the fish is the *Tilapia nilotica* or bolti fish. Noted for hatching its eggs in its mouth (see Cat. Nos. 27 and 55), it symbolized rebirth. Large bolti fish, as well as mullet, like the one represented in the second fish tile, were tasty foods to

the Deir el Medina workmen, who received a portion of their salary in fish. Mullet was also prized for its roe.

On the fourth tile, a woman crowned with an overpowering lotus flower appears to touch a stick to a tall flowering plant, perhaps a hollyhock. Its vertical format suggests it came from the lower half of a wall.

30

31

Material: Faience
Provenance: Pi-Ramesses (Qantir)
Length: 17.2 cm. (6.8 in.) to
  31.5 cm. (12.4 in.)
Width: 13.2 cm. (5.2 in.) to
  18.4 cm. (7.2 in.)
Thickness: 2.7 cm. (1.1 in.)
Date: New Kingdom, Dynasty XIX,
  Ramesses II
Cairo Accession Nos.: JE 89480,
  89479, 89484, 89483
Catalogue References:
  Brigham Young University Nos.
  11, 6, 5, 63
  Montreal and Vancouver Nos. 17,
  18, 19, 20

32

33

34
Floral Frieze

Remains of painted floral bands and garlands suspended blossom-downward from the upper edges of the house and temple walls indicate the most likely use for this brightly colored frieze of floral tile inlays, which once decorated a palace of Ramesses III in the Delta. Grape clusters and poppies alternately fill the spaces between large blue lotus flowers. Inset daisies mark the upper border. Each lotus and fruit cluster was individually made from a mold and then assembled. The daisies and poppies were made from a colored paste inlaid into the designated depressions in the matrix.

Material: Faience and glass paste
Provenance: Tell el Yahudiyah
Height: 7.7 cm. (3.03 in.)
Length: 60 cm. (23.6 in.)
Date: New Kingdom, Dynasty XX, Ramesses III
Cairo Accession No.: JE 21842
Catalogue References:
    Brigham Young University No. 10
    Montreal and Vancouver No. 22

35
Door from the Tomb of Sennedjem

The tomb of the deceased sheltered his body and soul and contained all that was necessary to sustain him in the afterlife. A locked door sealed it off from the secular world. This wooden example comes from the family tomb of Sennedjem, Servant in the Place of Truth, and it is the best preserved tomb door from Deir el Medina. A sliding bolt anchored it to the surrounding limestone frame, and a lump of clay impressed with an image of Anubis, jackal god of the necropolis (Cat. No. 36), sealed it.

On the outer face, upper register, a painted rectangular panel features Sennedjem, his wife Iyneferty and their daughter Nefer. They worship Osiris, god of fertility and resurrection, and Maat, goddess of Truth. Below, seven of Sennedjem's sons adore the composite funerary god Ptah-Sokar-Osiris and the mother goddess Isis. Burial equipment belonging to three of his sons, Khabekhnet, Khonsu, and Ramose, are also included in the exhibition (Cat. Nos. 36, 38, 39 and 40).

In keeping with ancient Egyptian tradition, Sennedjem and his sons have ruddy skin, reflecting their outdoor occupations. In contrast, his female family members, together with the two goddesses, have a lighter skin tone, since their primary tasks theoretically kept them indoors away from the sun. Osiris' green skin, recalling the color of new vegetation, reflects his role as fertility god.

Sennedjem and his family pose proudly in their finest pleated linen clothes. Normally white, these garments have acquired a yellowish tint, probably from the melting of the scented cone of grease which decorated their wigs.

On the inner face of the door, invisible to the outside world, a sacred game known as senet (see Cat. Nos. 24 and 36) is being played by Sennedjem and his wife against Fate, an invisible opponent. Should they win, their prize would be a blissful existence in the afterlife.

The distinctive palette of red and yellow ochre, aqua, and deep green displayed on the door is repeated inside on Sennedjem's tomb walls and echoed in most of the objects it contained (Cat. Nos. 9-11, 36-38, 40, and 42-45). It bears testimony to Sennedjem's skill as a painter and the high quality work of which the artisans of the time of Ramesses the Great were capable.

The Egyptian Antiquities Service excavated Sennedjem's tomb in 1886, one of precious few unplundered tombs at Thebes. When they removed the door and entered the burial chamber, an amazing sight greeted them. Nine family members in coffins and eleven more bodies wrapped in linen were stretched out on the ground. These represented three generations of Sennedjem's family. They also found household items and tools (Cat. Nos. 9-11, 41 and 45), as well as objects of exclusively funerary nature (Cat. Nos. 37-39, 41 and 44). Food for a splendid meal—breads, eggs, dates, doum palm nuts, and grains of wheat—was, of course, provided.

Material: Wood
Provenance: Thebes, Deir el Medina, Tomb of Sennedjem (T.T.1)
Height: 135 cm. (53.1 in.)
Width: 78 cm. (30.7 in.)
Date: New Kingdom, Dynasty XIX, Sety I-Ramesses II
Cairo Accession No.: JE 27303
Catalogue References: Brigham Young University No. 23 Montreal and Vancouver No. 45

163

Sarcophagus of Sennedjem's Son Khonsu

Following in his father's footsteps, Khonsu earned a place in the gang of Deir el Medina artisans, and like his father, he may have helped decorate and equip the tomb of Ramesses II. As oldest son, it was his job to prepare Sennedjem's burial. When Khonsu died at between 50 and 60 years of age, he was interred beside Sennedjem and other family members in their splendid tomb at Deir el Medina. His mummified body lay inside nested coffins (similar to Cat. Nos. 42-47) protected by this brilliantly painted sarcophagus. With its sloping lid rounded on one edge, it recalls the shape of the shrine of the vulture goddess of Upper Egypt, Nekhbet, which came to symbolize the Royal House of the South. (For the House of the North, see Cat. No. 39). A removable sledge on the bottom facilitated its transport from the place of mummification to the tomb.

The brilliantly decorated box may be read like a text book of the netherworld with funerary scenes illustrating spells from the Book of the Dead and their accompanying texts filling every available area. Isis, Nephthys, Selket, and Neith, four goddesses whose role was to protect the deceased, especially his internal organs, fill the end panels. Their green skin tone reflects their rejuvenative role (Cat. No. 35). Four ibis-headed deities bearing sky symbols frame the end of each side. Two sacred to the South are at the front (head) end; two sacred to the North protect the feet. This prob-

ably corresponded to the orientation of the sarcophagus inside the tomb. The four sons of the god Horus who face the southern, "front" end guarded the deceased's internal organs.

Two registers make up the central panel on each side. On the "east" face, not shown, two geni bearing *ankhs*, the hieroglyph for life, squat in front of a low building. Behind are two Nile gods whose fleshy breasts and protruding bellies symbolize the fertility brought yearly by the flood waters.

Below, Khonsu kneels in adoration beside the mother goddess and mistress of the sky, Hathor, represented as a cow. Beside Hathor, Khonsu accompanied by his wife Tameket, plays a game of senet (Cat. Nos. 24 and 35).

On the central panel on the "west" face, not shown, Khonsu worships two lions who guard the rising sun. A sign of life hangs between the two horizons, which define the borders of the world. One lion faces Khonsu, the other faces the head of the falcon god Horus rising from the primeval pool of water which originally covered the entire land. Hathor, behind Horus, protects him.

Below, Isis and Nephthys squat at either end of a decorated shrine. Inside, Anubis, the jackal-headed god of mummification, attends the body of Khonsu, stretched out on a lion bed. The five jars beneath probably contained the magical oils and unguents guaranteed to assure Khonsu's rebirth. On the far end, two *bas*,

human headed birds representing the souls of Khonsu and his wife, perch atop a low building beside a pile of offerings symbolic of renewed life.

Protecting the body of Khonsu from the top of the lid of his sarcophagus are, on one side, two representations of Anubis shown this time as a jackal-like dog squatting on a bier. Anubis' alert watchful pose reflects his role as guardian of the necropolis. On the other side is a figure of the sky goddess Nut. Her winged arms stretch out in readiness to receive Khonsu and welcome him to her abode. Also present are, once again, the four sons of Horus and additional representations of Khonsu and his wife.

Rich in symbolism and representing a highpoint in funerary art, Khonsu's sarcophagus protected his mortal remains from the time of Ramesses the Great until their discovery by the Egyptian Antiquities Service in 1886. The coffins which were placed inside the sarcophagus and the mask which covered his face may be seen in the Metropolitan Museum of Art. Khonsu is also represented in his brother Khabekhnet's tomb.

Material: Wood
Provenance: Thebes, Deir el Medina, Tomb of Sennedjem (T.T.1)
Height: 125 cm. (49.2 in.)
Length including Runner: 262 cm. (103.1 in.)
Width: 98 cm. (38.6 in.)
Date: New Kingdom, Dynasty XIX, Sety I-Ramesses II
Cairo Accession No.: JE 27302
Catalogue References:
    Brigham Young University No. 24
    Montreal and Vancouver No. 48

37, 38
Shawabtis of Sennedjem and Ramose

While the deceased enjoyed every possible pleasure in the afterlife, miniature servant figures called shawabtis took care of any work that awaited. Sennedjem's shawabti is shown here, as well as one belonging to his son, Ramose. Their poses and attributes are characteristic of shawabtis, namely, they are wrapped as mummies, and their crossed arms clutch agricultural tools (in this case, two hoes). A bag to carry grain is often suspended on the back (Sennedjem's shawabti carries two). A total of nine shawabtis of Sennedjem and three shawabtis of Ramose were found in Sennedjem's family tomb. It was customary later on to provide one shawabti for each day of the year and one supervisor shawabti for every ten workers, a total of 401. Kings included shawabtis in their burial equipment, often in even greater numbers.

Eight lines of inscription encircling Sennedjem's shawabti contain the traditional shawabti prayer excerpted from Chapter Six of the *Book of the Dead:*

O shawabti! If the Osiris Sennedjem is called upon to do any of the work which a man does in the necropolis, namely to cultivate the fields, to water the banks, to transport sand from the East to the West, "Here I am!" you shall say.

The inscription on Ramose's shawabti contains only his name and his epithet, Child of the Tomb, signifying that his father Sennedjem was part of the gang of Deir el Medina workmen charged with construction of the royal tombs. In all likelihood, he died before he could follow in his father's footsteps. Ramose stands fifth in line on the outside of his family tomb door (Cat. No. 35, lower register).

37
Material: Limestone
Provenance: Thebes, Deir el Medina, Tomb of Sennedjem (T.T.1)
Height: 29 cm. (11.4 in.)
Date: New Kingdom, Dynasty XIX, Sety I-Ramesses II
Cairo Accession No.: JE 27251 = CG 47740
Catalogue References: Brigham Young University No. 30 Montreal and Vancouver No. 52

38
Material: Limestone
Provenance: Thebes, Deir el Medina, Tomb of Sennedjem (T.T.1)
Height: 19 cm. (7.5 in.)
Date: New Kingdom, Dynasty XIX, Sety I-Ramesses II
Cairo Accession No.: JE 27232 = CG 47765
Catalogue References: Brigham Young University No. 29 Montreal and Vancouver No. 51

In the New Kingdom special care was taken with shawabtis (Cat. Nos. 37-38), and they were often stored in pairs in chests similar in shape to this one. Later, shawabtis were mass-produced and stored by the hundreds in crude, often undecorated wooden boxes. In this splendid example, the vaulted lid, vertical projections, and "palace facade" decoration imitate the appearance of the sanctuary of Lower Egypt sacred to the cobra goddess Wadjet, which was often juxtaposed with the holy shrine of Upper Egypt (Cat. Nos. 25 and 36). Together, they brought to mind the duality of the country united under a single divine monarch. The box/shrine rests on runners, which here are strictly ornamental, but on larger items (Cat. No. 36) would have facilitated transport across the sand. One Deir el Medina villager exchanged the equivalent of two deben of copper (182 grams) to obtain a shawabti box, and a record of this transaction was inscribed on an ostracon (Cat. Nos. 53 and 57).

A central column of inscription on each side of the shawabti box identifies its owner, "The Revered One under Osiris (god of the netherworld) Khabekhnet, justified." Khabekhnet, the eldest of Sennedjem's seven sons and one of ten children, is represented on the outside door of his father's family tomb (Cat. No. 35, bottom register, first in line). Many objects belonging to Khabekhnet were found inside, including a painted wooden chest in the exhibition (Cat. No. 40). His own tomb lay next door. Most likely, he was born during the reign of Sety I and was active during Ramesses II's rule.

Material: Wood
Provenance: Thebes, Deir el Medina, Tomb of Sennedjem (T.T.1)
Height: 30 cm. (11.8 in.)
Date: New Kingdom, Dynasty XIX, Sety I-Ramesses II
Cairo Accession No.: JE 27296
Catalogue References:
  Brigham Young University No. 22
  Montreal and Vancouver No. 50

40
Khabekhnet's Chest

Linen, jewelry, cosmetic articles, and other personal effects were frequently stored in boxes such as this one. Made of pieces of local wood doweled together, it has been painted to appear as if it were fabricated from costly imported woods and ivory, a common trick of crafty Egyptian woodworkers. The lid of the chest pivoted upward from the front to reveal four compartments inside. To fasten it, a cord was wound alternately around the two knobs and then sealed with a lump of wet clay which was probably impressed with its proprietor's stamp.

Two lines of inscription on the lid identify the owners as Khabekhnet, Sennedjem's eldest son (see also Cat. Nos. 35 and 39) and his wife Sahto. The couple resided in Deir el Medina in a house located close to Sennedjem's.

Similarly, Khabekhnet's tomb was near his father's (and other family members), and both shared the same chapel. A number of objects belonging to Khabekhnet, including this box, eight shawabtis (Cat. Nos. 37 and 38) and a shawabti box (Cat. No. 39) were found in Sennedjem's tomb. Like all of the more-than-forty wooden boxes from that tomb, this one was empty at the time of discovery.

Material: Wood
Provenance: Thebes, Deir el Medina, Tomb of Sennedjem (T.T.1)
Length: 28 cm. (11.02 in.)
Width: 20 cm. (7.9 in.)
Height: 17 cm. (6.7 in.)
Date: New Kingdom, Dynasty XIX, Sety I-Ramesses II
Cairo Accession No.: JE 27292
Catalogue References:
 Brigham Young University No. 34
 Montreal and Vancouver No. 43

41
Sennedjem's Immitation Stone Vessel

Artisans of the New Kingdom mastered the art of clever copying, a technique practiced almost since the beginning of recorded history in Egypt. Precious stones were imitated in glass and faience; cheap local woods were veneered in imported ebony and ivory; and pottery was painted to look like stone. Here, a simple buff-colored ceramic vessel resembles veined alabaster through the addition of white paint and multi-colored wavy lines. A ceramic disk painted with an abstract floral design forms the lid. The inscription identifies Sennedjem as the vessel's owner.

The bag-like shape, called an alabastron, is typically Egyptian and seems, in some instances, to have contained scented fat (Cat. No. 48). In the New Kingdom many examples were manufactured in stone and faience as well as pottery. Through trade, some found their way to the Aegean world where they were copied in local materials.

Material: Pottery
Provenance: Thebes, Deir el Medina, Tomb of Sennedjem (T.T.1)
Height: 14.5 cm. (5.7 in.)
Date: New Kingdom, Dynasty XIX, Sety I-Ramesses II
Cairo Accession No.: JE 27248
Catalogue References:
  Brigham Young University No. 36
  Montreal and Vancouver No. 49

Lid From the Outer Coffin of Sennedjem

The mummified body of the "Servant in the Place of Truth" Sennedjem was placed inside an outer coffin and inner lid of anthropoid shape. These were housed inside a rectangular sarcophagus similar to Khonsu's (Cat. No. 36). Shown here is the stuccoed wooden lid of Sennedjem's outer coffin. He is represented as a mummy with his arms crossed on his chest clasping the *tyet* amulet in one hand and the *djed* pillar in the other. Associated with Isis and Osiris, they symbolize protection and stability, respectively. Crisscrossed columns of inscription on the coffin's surface imitate the pattern of a mummy's outer bandaging. Sennedjem wears an elaborately curled wig, a floral headband, a broad floral collar, and a short false beard. Hands, amulets, face, and beard were made separately and attached to the body of the coffin.

Funerary images decorate the length of the coffin. The winged sky goddess Nut stretches protectively across Sennedjem's chest. Beneath, in mirror images on each side, are representations of the guardian of the necropolis Anubis, kneeling goddesses touching *shen* signs (Cat. Nos. 8 and 72) symbolic of protection and rebirth, and of Sennedjem drinking eternally from the sweet waters provided by the goddess of the sycamore tree. Although all the other images are fairly rigid and stereotyped, this last vignette displays a much freer naturalistic treatment. On one side Sennedjem's wig is black; on the opposite side it is white. Finally, the goddess Nephthys on top of his head and Isis on the soles of his feet serve as divine mourners. They ensure that Sennedjem's body will be protected in its journey through the netherworld.

Material: Wood
Provenance: Thebes, Deir el Medina, Tomb of Sennedjem (T.T.1)
Length: 185 cm. (72.8 in.)
Width: 50 cm. (19.7 in.)
Date: New Kingdom, Dynasty XIX, Sety I-Ramesses II
Cairo Accession No.: JE 27308
Catalogue References:
   Brigham Young University No. 25
   Montreal and Vancouver No. 33

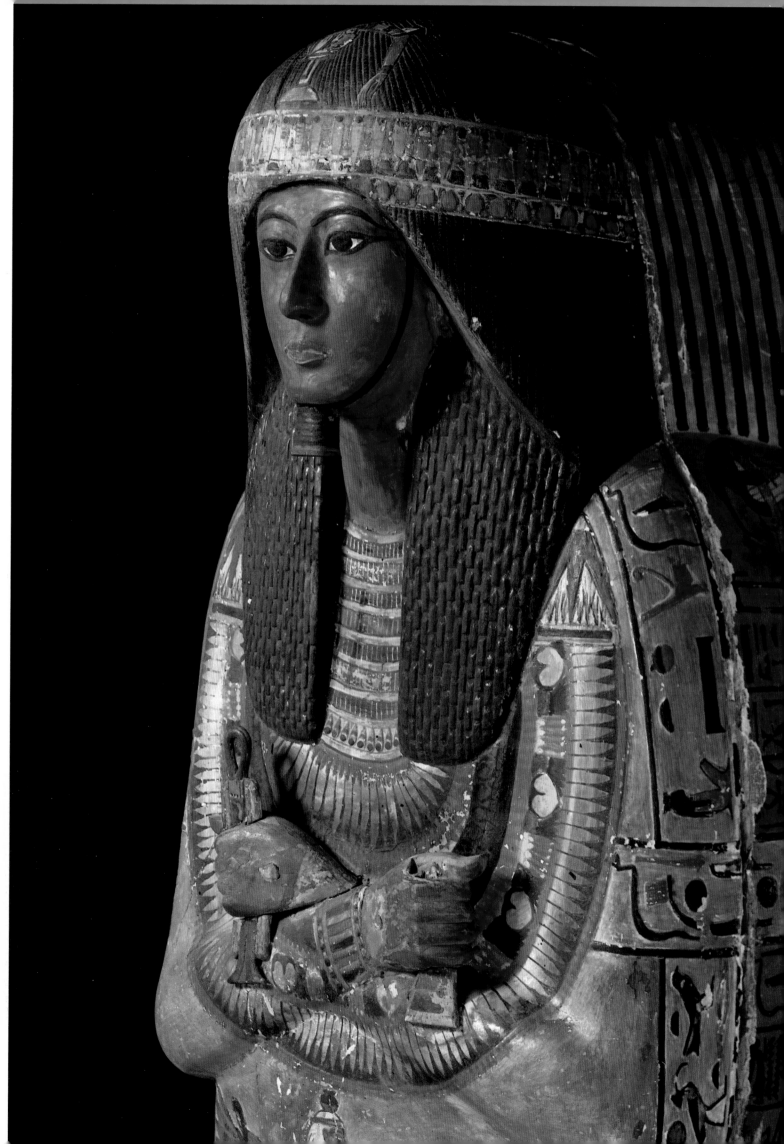

43

Inner Lid from Sennedjem's Coffin

Alert and youthful, Sennedjem's face gazes intently at the outside world from a lid which protected his mummy. Like his outer coffin (Cat. No. 42), it was made from stuccoed, painted, and varnished wood. Of the two, this is the most lifelike. Following contemporary custom, he wears a garment and wig similar to what he would have worn in life. His three-quarter length kilt would have been made from two pieces of finely spun, undyed linen. The first was wrapped around his waist tightly and secured. The second, a long narrow strip with fringed ends, was twisted around his waist and hips and looped underneath to form an apron.

In life Sennedjem's wig would most likely have been made from human hair, with each strand carefully curled and secured to a matrix, perhaps with beeswax. As on his outer coffin, he wears a short beard and a floral and bead collar.

The column of inscription between Sennedjem's feet identifies him as a "Servant in the Place of Truth" in Western Thebes (i.e. a worker at Deir el Medina). Isis, painted at the bottom of his feet, grants Sennedjem her eternal protection.

Material: Wood
Provenance: Thebes, Deir el
  Medina, Tomb of Sennedjem
  (T.T.1)
Length: 175 cm. (69.9 in.)
Width: 44.3 cm. (17.4 in.)
Date: New Kingdom, Dynasty XIX,
  Sety I-Ramesses II
Cairo Accession No.: JE 27308
Catalogue References:
  Brigham Young University No. 26
  Montreal and Vancouver No. 34

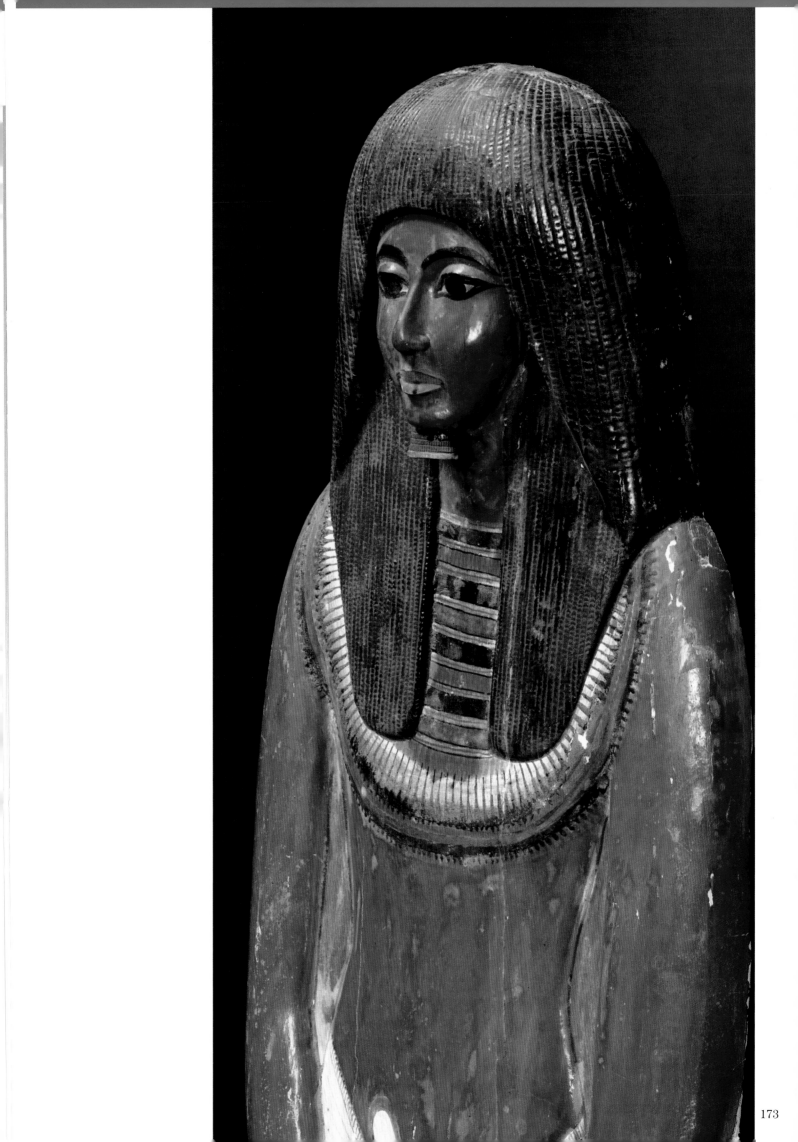

Alabaster Vessel of Ramesses II

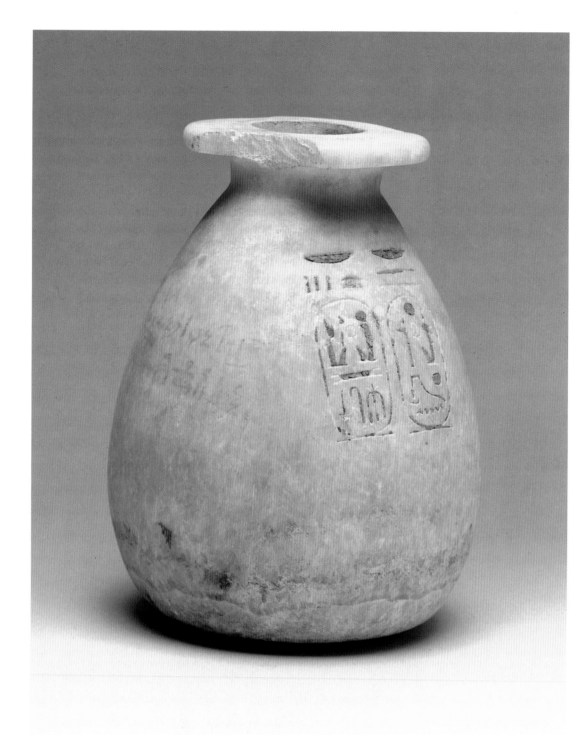

Since Ramesses the Great's tomb suffered near-total destruction at the hands of ancient plunderers, nothing remains that can unquestionably be identified as having been buried with the king (Cat. No. 50), except for a few of his shawabtis. However, since this alabaster vessel bears two incised and inlaid cartouches of Ramesses II and since it was found in the Valley of the Kings beside the tomb of Merneptah not far from Ramesses II's tomb, it possibly was part of Ramesses II's original burial equipment. Perhaps plunderers tossed it aside so as not to be burdened by its weight after they had emptied it of its precious contents. Alternatively, it may have contained some of the embalming materials of the king, which were buried together with the remains of his funerary feast following the burial ceremony.

Vessels of this shape, called alabastra, were common in Egypt in Dynasties XVIII and XIX and could be made from clay as well as stone (Cat. No. 41). They were often sealed with simple, disk-shaped lids. An analysis of the contents of similarly shaped vessels indicates that some held scented unguents intended for a cosmetic or ritual purpose.

Material: Alabaster inlaid with
    paste
Provenance: Thebes, Valley of the
    Kings
Height: 26.6 cm. (10.5 in.)
Date: New Kingdom, Dynasty XIX,
    Ramesses II
Cairo Accession No.: JE 46712
Catalogue References:
    Brigham Young University No. 13
    Montreal and Vancouver No. 44

Egyptian goldsmiths ranked among the finest in the ancient world, and nowhere is their skill better displayed than in this pair of bracelets which bear the coronation name of Ramesses II. Forming the central element of each is a pair of ducks with recurved heads, the characteristic position for ducks intended as offerings to the gods. A large inlay of lapis lazuli, positioned in the center of the bracelet's widest part, functions as the back of the paired golden birds. The interplay of color between the shiny gold and deep blue highlights each to their best advantage. Highly prized both for its rich color and its rarity, lapis had to be imported from mines in Afghanistan. Most of it was probably traded along the Euphrates River and reached Egypt from there.

The heads and tails of the ducks and the bands of the bracelets are made of high carat gold which ancient craftsmen hammered, soldered, and twisted into shape. Another technique employed here was granulation, a process by which minute gold balls were fused onto a flat gold surface when both were heated to the proper temperature. Each band of the bracelet was manufactured in two matching semicircles. One side hinged together permanently; the other opened or closed by means of a locking pin. Tomb paintings, statues, and the mummy of King Tutankhamun provide evidence that both men and women often wore the bracelets in multiples.

Construction workers found these splendid jewels at Bubastis together with Cat. Nos. 62, 68 and 70. Either they were made for Ramesses II himself or for a temple statue he commissioned.

Since other items in the hoard bore the cartouches of Queen Tausert (Cat. No. 70), these precious objects cannot have been buried prior to her reign (1188-1187 B.C.). Accordingly, Ramesses II's bracelets must have been retained as family heirlooms.

Material: Gold and lapis lazuli
Provenance: Bubastis
Width: 6 cm. (2.4 in.)
Maximum Diam.: 6.5 cm. (2.6 in.)
Date: New Kingdom, Dynasty XIX, Ramesses II
Cairo Accession No.: JE 39873 = CG 52575 and CG 52576
Catalogue References:
  Brigham Young University No. 49
  Montreal and Vancouver No. 23

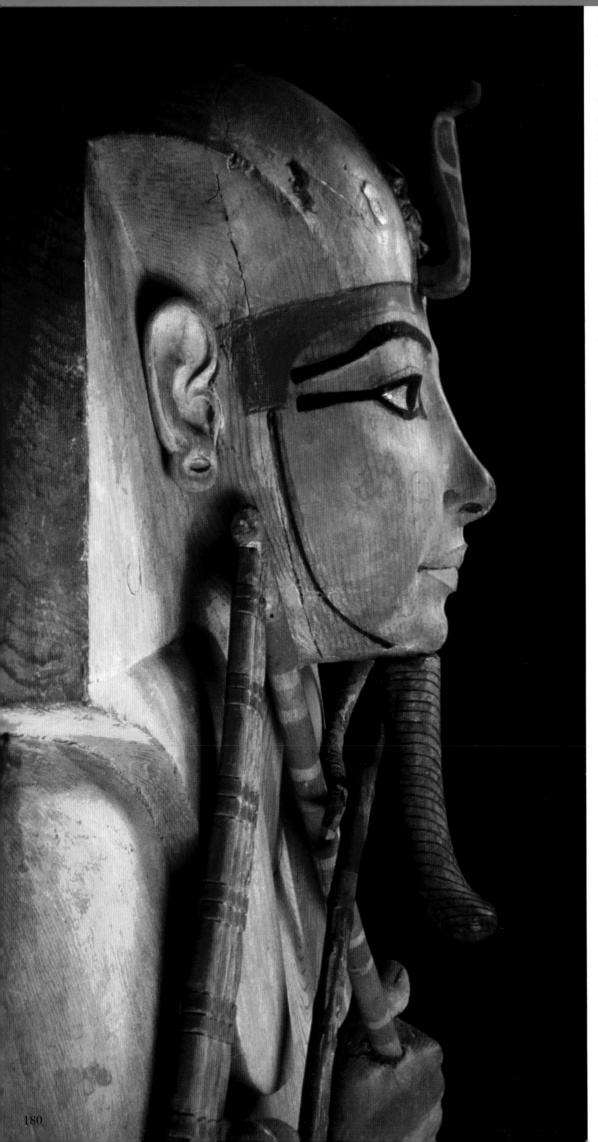

Lid from the Coffin of Ramesses the Great

Of all the gold, costly jewels, and other precious equipment that surely accompanied Ramesses II in his tomb, little remains that can be identified with certainty (Cat. No. 48). Although this cedar lid covered his mummy, the soft treatment of the facial features leaves little doubt that it was made for one of Ramesses II's royal predecessors, either in the late Eighteenth or early Nineteenth Dynasty, perhaps for his grandfather, Ramesses I. The wood was imported from Lebanon. A hurriedly inked inscription on the legs and on top of the head records its painful history.

Stripped of all valuables in the two centuries following his death, Ramesses II's desecrated body, together with those of several other prominent kings, was rewrapped and moved to Sety I's tomb by order of the High Priest of Amun, Herihor. This took place in Year Twenty-Four of Ramesses XI (ca. 1075 B.C.), on the Fifteenth day of the Third month of *Peret*. Still vulnerable, it was moved yet again to a safer stronghold in the tomb of Queen Inhapy, just south of Deir el Bahari together with nearly forty other royal mummies. This trip occupied three days in the Fourth month of *Peret* in the Tenth Year of the reign of Siamun (ca. 969 B.C.), from day Seventeen through Twenty. There they remained until their discovery in A.D. 1881.

This coffin lid probably resembles the way one of Ramesses II's coffin lids would have looked stripped of its gold and inlaid precious stone covering. The crossed hands, a characteristic pose of royal mummies, hold the crook and flail of rulership (probably added during one of the reburials). A divine cobra (uraeus) emerges from the front of the royal head-cloth *(nemes)* to shelter and protect the king.

Material: Wood
Provenance: Thebes, near Deir el Bahari
Height: 206 cm. (81.1 in.)
Width: 54.5 cm. (21.5 in.)
Depth at Foot: 36.5 cm. (14.4 in.)
Date: Coffin: New Kingdom, Dynasty XVIII or XIX
Inscriptions: New Kingdom and Third Intermediate Period, Dynasty XX and Dynasty XXI
Cairo Accession No.: JE 26214 = CG 61020
Catalogue References:
Brigham Young University No. 55
Montreal and Vancouver No. 66

55
Faience Bowl

Filled with aquatic motifs painted in black against a blue-glazed background, this bowl belongs to a type common in New Kingdom tombs and temples. It probably contained a rejuvenative liquid refreshment, perhaps milk, wine, or water, intended either for the deceased or for the gods.

Although water, indicated by wavy lines, is shown only in the rectangular pool in the center, the entirety of the bowl's interior represents a pond. Decorative but symbolic as well, the images inside relate to the theme of rebirth. The lotus flowers radiating from each corner of the central rectangle suggest rejuvenation: they close each evening to reopen with the dawning of a new day just as the sun god was reborn every morning. On two sides of the pool, bolti fish *(Tilapia nilotica)* nibble lotus buds. The Egyptians noted that these fish incubate and hatch their eggs inside their mouths. The tiny newborns emerging suggest an image of spontaneous generation and fertility. Associated with the goddess Hathor, they formed a duality with the sun god as represented by the lotus flower. Stylized palmettes occupying the remaining space symbolize the tree of life.

Material: Faience
Provenance: Thebes, Deir el Medina (Tomb No. 1382)
Diameter: 17 cm. (6.7 in.)
Date: New Kingdom, Dynasty XVIII
Cairo Accession No.: JE 63677
Catalogue References:
  Brigham Young University No. 39
  Montreal and Vancouver No. 41

56
Boat Procession

Egyptian gods routinely resided in their temple homes hidden from public view; however, on special holidays priests brought them outside their sacred compounds. Cult images were available for all to revere, and religion became a participatory event.

Represented here is a scene from a summer holiday known as the ''Beautiful Feast of the Valley'' when the god Amun-Ra left his home at Karnak temple and travelled across the river on a great barge known as the *Userhet* to visit the royal funerary temples on the West Bank. On land he was transported in a veiled sanctuary placed on a portable boat-shrine. Here, in the upper register, the boat is borne on the shoulders of twenty-four priests and privileged high dignitaries. According to the text, many of the officials who carried the portable barque filled important positions at Deir el Medina, the village of workmen who built the royal tombs. Images of Amun-Ra shown as a ram (Cat. No. 53) decorate both bow and stern. The sacred barque, having just left one temporary resting place and on its way to another, is met by Ramesses II's father, Sety I, who offers burning incense to the divine image. Below, the royal scribe Amunemonet kneels in adoration of the great *Userhet* and recites a prayer in honor of the Great God. A description of the *Userhet* of Ramesses III (1185-1154 B.C.) from the Harris Papyrus hints at the grandeur of this divine barque. Measuring 67 meters in length, it was made of imported Lebanese cedar covered with gold and other precious materials.

All could take part in the Beautiful Feast of the Valley by greeting the god in his journey. By means of an oracle, the god would answer their questions. Villagers marked the celebration's end with banquets held at the tombs of their deceased relatives. Drunkenness was encouraged since it broke down the barriers between the living and the dead. After an evening filled with abundant food, drink, and revelry, they customarily passed the night in the ancestral funerary chapels.

Material: Limestone
Provenance: Thebes, Deir el Medina
Approx. Height: 60 cm. (23.6 in.)
Approx. Width: 80 cm. (31.5 in.)
Date: New Kingdom, Dynasty XIX, Sety I—Ramesses II (Year I)
Cairo Accession No.: JE 43591
Catalogue References:
Brigham Young University No. 46
Montreal and Vancouver No. 11

57

Harpist Ostracon

A squatting, bald, middle-aged man wearing a long linen garment (see Cat. No. 8) plays the harp in this quick sketch on a scrap of limestone, known as an ostracon (Cat. No. 53). The harp was probably made from wood covered in painted leather. Fourteen alternating black and red pegs on top secured the gut strings, twelve of which are represented. (Harps with as many as sixteen strings were known.) To what notes the strings were tuned, we do not know, since no musical notation has been found in ancient Egypt.

The harper shown here may have been blind. In many representations, harpers clearly lacked sight, perhaps to avoid confronting the gods directly when they played before them. Whether or not harpers actually were blinded is not known.

Harps might be strummed while seated or standing. A different type of harp was balanced on the shoulder. Both men and women played the harp either in orchestras or individually, perhaps accompanying their own voice. Some harper's songs show a philosophical contemplation of the fleeting quality of life and a despair at the chances of achieving immortality; others glorified death and assisted the deceased on his netherworld journey; and yet others advocated living life to its fullest, pursuing one's desires.

Material: Limestone
Provenance: Thebes, Deir el Medina
Height: 13.8 cm. (5.4 in.)
Width: 11 cm. (4.3 in.)
Date: New Kingdom, Dynasty XX
Cairo Accession No.: JE 69409
Catalogue References:
  Brigham Young University No. 43
  Montreal and Vancouver No. 14

58
Clappers

For ceremonial dances and orchestral performances accompanying banquets, the staccato beating together of clappers supplied rhythm and punctuation. Their armlike form suggests they were inspired by the clapping of hands. Incised lines around the wrists represent bracelets. A cord threaded through holes at the ends kept the clappers together when not in use.

Judging from representations in painting and relief, women and especially young girls most often played clappers. Frequently, other musicians performing on harps, lutes, lyres, and oboes accompanied them. Drums, trumpets, tambourines, and sistra were also played. In fact, early forms of most modern instruments were in use in ancient Egypt, although not necessarily in the same manner. In many instances, the instruments themselves as well as their representations have been found, but time and weather have changed them significantly so we cannot be sure how they sounded.

Music not only delighted an audience but also served an important religious function. Sweet melodic tones could be counted on to soothe an angry god or goddess and also drive away evil spirits. A number of deities, both male and female, were associated with music, and the playing of musical instruments was considered a priestly duty (Cat. No. 2).

Material: Bone or ivory
Provenance: Thebes
Length; 17.5 cm. (6.9 in.)
Date: New Kingdom
Cairo Accession No.: JE 25820 = CG 69211
Catalogue References:
  Brigham Young University No. 44
  Montreal and Vancouver No. 12

59, 60, 61
Sun Sanctuary from Abu Simbel

The cult of the sun may be traced back to the beginning of Egyptian civilization. Ramesses the Great, like many of his royal ancestors, elevated the sun god Ra-Horakhty to a position of importance. Cut into the rock at the north end of the Great Temple terrace at Abu Simbel was a sanctuary devoted to the worship of the sun. Alternating statues of Ramesses II and Ra-Horakhty stood beside it.

Cliffs border the chapel to the west and north. To the east is a pylon. Normally taking the form of two towers with a gateway between them, here the pylon lacks an opening. Entry into this unroofed chapel was through a door in the terrace and up a short flight of stairs. A sandstone altar cut from the living rock stood inside. Two obelisks flanked its north side.

The sloping sides of the top of the obelisks recalled the pyramidal shape of the *benben* stone and caught the morning sun's first rays. Four baboons perch atop the altar with arms upraised in worship. As the sun rose each morning, the baboons' shrill cry awakened the world to a new day. Behind the altar, an open air shrine housed a scarab beetle surmounted by a sun disk and a single squatting baboon wearing a lunar disk and crescent. The scarab placed on the east side represented the rising sun, newly reborn and rejuvenated on the eastern horizon, as the Egyptians hoped they, too, would be. The baboon on the west symbolized the moon and night. On the outside of the shrine nearest the scarab is a representation of Ramesses II offering to the sun god Ra-Horakhty, and on the side nearest the baboon, the king makes an offering to the moon god Thoth shown in an alternate form, namely an ibis-headed man.

Found in 1909, this is the most complete sun sanctuary of its kind known to date, and its form is unique. One can still imagine the awe inspired by the rising sun as its rays burst through the towers of the false pylon, rose between the upraised paws of the adoring baboons, and illuminated the cult images inside the shrine.

Material: Sandstone
Provenance: Abu Simbel
59
Height of Baboons: 92 cm.
  (36.2 in.) to 99 cm. (39 in.)
Base Lengths: 37 cm. (14.6 in.) to
  43 cm. (16.9 in.)
Base Widths: 26 cm. (10.2 in.) to
  28 cm. (11.02 in.)
60
Height of Seated Baboon: 92 cm.
  (36.2 in.)
Base Width of Seated Baboon:
  33 cm. (12.99 in.)
61
Height of Scarab: 69 cm. (27.2 in.)
Width of Scarab: 43 cm. (16.9 in.)
Date: New Kingdom, Dynasty XIX,
  Ramesses II
Cairo Accession No.: JE 42955
Catalogue References:
  Brigham Young University No. 47
  Montreal and Vancouver No. 2

62

Goat Vessel

A masterpiece of crafts-manship, this gold and silver vessel reflects the cosmopol-itan nature of the Egyptian empire in the Ramesside Era. Since its primary metal, silver, was rare in Egypt, it was most likely imported from the Near East. The gold used on the rim and handle was probably mined in Nubia, Egypt's chief source of that material, although the animal handle motif is primarily Near Eastern. In shape, the vessel recalls the pomegranate, an exotic fruit to the Egyptians. It was first brought to Egypt from the Levant in the early Eight-eenth Dynasty.

In the upper register of the rim's incised decoration, stylized palmettes, a motif borrowed from Near Eastern art, frame scenes of animal combat. Also present is a winged griffin, a mythical creature whose origins may also lie in ancient Mesopotamia or Iran. The register below likewise displays hunting and combat, but it is purely Egyptian in inspiration and has a riverine rather than desert location. Scenes of fishing and bird trapping in the Nile marshes symbolize royal mastery over the country and victory over its enemies.

An incised rectangle on the belly of the vessel depicts the Royal Butler Atum-em-ta-neb, the owner, wearing a traditional long, pleated linen garment and worshipping a foreign god-dess. The inscription expres-ses Atum-em-ta-neb's (and every Egyptian's) desire to enjoy millions of years of life and power.

Rearing on his hind legs and nipping at the rim of the vessel as if to drink from it is a goat hammered out of sheet gold which forms the handle. Although the goat's body is made out of two halves of metal, fine crafts-manship makes the join prac-tically invisible.

Undoubtedly as much of a treasure to its original owner as it is today, this vessel was part of a group of precious objects found in two caches at Bubastis (modern Zagazig) in 1906, when con-struction workers were build-ing a railroad (see also Cat. Nos. 49, 68 and 70). Two objects in the group were inscribed for Queen Tausert (Cat. No. 70), and it is on that basis that this vessel may be dated.

Material: Gold and silver
Provenance: Bubastis
Height: 16.5 cm. (6.5 in.)
Height of Handle: 9.5 cm. (3.7 in.)
Opening Diam.: 8.9 cm. (3.5 in.)
Date: New Kingdom, Dynasty XIX,
    Queen Tausert
Cairo Accession No.: JE 39867 =
    CG 53262
Catalogue References:
    Brigham Young University No. 51
    Montreal and Vancouver No. 16

63, 64
Offering Jar and Basin of Psusennes I

Cleanliness of the gods and those who served them played an important role in Egyptian religious practices. Daily, priests bathed in the sacred lake attached to major temples and used its waters to wash the gods' cult statues. For ritual washing, possibly in connection with meals, a jar to pour water and a basin to catch it were used. Frequently, they appear together on tomb or temple walls.

The jar with its squat body, long neck, and papyrus-umbel spout was hammered from a single piece of sheet gold. The basin also was made in one piece with the exception of the handle. For the latter, artisans skillfully bound together bud and flower of the lotus on top, and then underneath, terminated the stem in a stylized palm motif. Three gold rivets bond handle and basin.

The juxtaposition of the papyrus on the jar spout and the lotus of the basin handle recalls the union of Lower (Delta) and Upper (Nile Valley) Egypt respectively, as they do on Cat. No. 70.

Both jar and basin feature the throne name and birth name of Psusennes I, in whose tomb they, like Cat. Nos. 65, 66 and 69 were found.

Material: Gold
Provenance: Tanis
Jar Height: 38 cm. (14.96 in.)
Jar Max. Diam.: 8.9 cm. (3.5 in.)
Basin Height: 17 cm. (6.7 in.)
Basin Diam.: 10.2 cm. (4.01 in.)
Date: Third Intermediate Period,
   Dynasty XXI, Psusennes I
   (1054-1004 BC)
Cairo Accession Nos.: JE 85892 (jar);
   JE 85893 (basin)
Catalogue References:
   Brigham Young University
   Nos. 14, 15
   Montreal and Vancouver
   Nos. 30, 31

65
Psusennes I's Gold of Valor

Brilliant and massive, this golden collar is the best example of a type represented frequently in the New Kingdom. Known as the *shebyu* or Gold of Valor, it was worn by the king, by a god, or by a fortunate official who received it in return for bravery on the battlefield or a similar act of courage or honor. This example was one of three found on the mummy of King Psusennes I in 1940.

Approximately nineteen pounds (8.6 kilograms) of gold comprise the necklace as it now exists. Five circlets of flat gold disk beads (approximately 5,000) strung on heavy thread fasten to a lapis lazuli-inlaid gold plaque, which also serves as the clasp. Originally, there were six circlets. Suspended from the plaque are fourteen braided gold chains; each divides into two and then four narrow ropes. Gold floral elements neatly mask each transition and also form the bottom border.

The cartouches of Psusennes I make up the gold plaque's central element of decoration. Divided by a papyrus column, the cartouches are framed by friezes of cobras wearing sun disks. A winged scarab pushing a sun disk, a symbol of dawn and rebirth (Cat. No. 61), crowns this baroque melange.

Material: Gold and lapis lazuli
Provenance: Tanis
Total Height: 64.5 cm. (25.4 in.)
Opening Diam.: 13.5 cm. (5.3 in.)
Chain Length: 30.7 cm. (12.1 in.)
Date: Third Intermediate Period,
   Dynasty XXI, Psusennes I
Cairo Accession No.: JE 85571
Catalogue References:
   Brigham Young University No. 48
   Montreal and Vancouver No. 32

66
Offering Dish and Stand of Psusennes I

Not only the king but all who could afford it consecrated offerings to the gods hoping to receive divine favor and a good life in return. Frequently on temple and tomb walls as well as on humble private stelae, one or more gods are seated beside a table piled high with meats, vegetables, fruits, breads, beverages, flowers—all the products of a rich and fertile land. This offering stand resembles the one shown in many of these representations.

The stand itself is a hollow silver tube with a narrow neck and flaring base. Set into it is a slightly concave dish with a deep central depression, intended perhaps for catching liquids. A column of elegantly engraved hieroglyphs on the stand includes the titulary of the king who probably commissioned it, namely Psusennes I, and notes his desire to be in the good graces of Osiris, Master of Eternity, and Wen-nefer, Ruler of the Living. Inside the dish, the king's names are repeated beside an invocation to the Memphite god Ptah-Sokar. Since all the deities mentioned are funerary in character, this offering stand likely formed part of the king's burial equipment. In 1940 a French expedition found these items in the tomb of Psusennes I on top of a bronze brazier which bore the name of his revered ancestor, Ramesses II (see also Cat. Nos. 63-65 and 69).

Material: Silver
Provenance: Tanis
Height: 59.5 cm. (23.4 in.)
Diam. at top of Base: 8.5 cm. (3.3 in.)
Depth of Dish: 8 cm. (3.1 in.)
Top Diam.: 25.7 cm. (10.1 in.)
Date: Third Intermediate Period, Dynasty XXI, Psusennes I
Cairo Accession No.: JE 86899
Catalogue References:
  Brigham Young University No. 18
  Montreal and Vancouver No. 29

67
Earrings of King Sety II

Men, as well as women, pierced their ears in ancient Egypt, and by the late New Kingdom they could choose from a variety of earrings, earplugs, and ear studs. These tube-and-boss earrings, which bear the cartouches of King Sety II (1200-1194 B.C.), represent some of the most ornate known. The upper element actually includes two halves, each consisting of a hollow tube attached to a boss, one hemispherical in shape and the other floral. Since one tube is slightly smaller in diameter, they fit neatly and securely together. The middle element is a trapezoidal plaque looped over the bar between the bosses. A rounded area cut out at the top accommodated the earlobe. Dangling from the bot-

tom are seven cornflowers, fashioned, like the rest of the pieces, out of sheet gold.

Found in a small pit, numbered 56, in the Valley of the Kings, these earrings were part of a cache of precious metal jewelry and funerary objects inscribed primarily for Sety II and his wife, Tausert.

A few objects which bore the cartouches of Ramesses II may have been cherished heirlooms of Sety II's great royal ancestor. The ownership of the funerary deposit and why this glittering hoard was deposited in it remains a mystery.

His mummy shows that Ramesses II had pierced ears, as did his father Sety I, and son and successor Merneptah. Frequently, kings of the New Kingdom from

late Dynasty XVIII on are represented with pierced ears. Nevertheless, we really have no evidence that adult male rulers (unlike non-royal males) ever wore earrings.

Material: Gold
Provenance: Thebes, Valley of the
    Kings
Height: 13.5 cm. (5.3 in.)
Length: 5 cm. (1.96 in.)
Date: New Kingdom, Dynasty XIX,
    Sety II
Cairo Accession No.: JE 39675 =
    CG 52397 and CG 52398
Catalogue References:
    Brigham Young University No. 53
    Montreal and Vancouver No. 24

68
Gold and
Carnelian Collar

Based on representations in sculpture, relief, and painting, multi-row broad collars were the most common jewelry item in ancient Egypt. Worn at banquets, festivals, and other ceremonial occasions, they also formed part of the funerary equipment.

In the New Kingdom, especially, collars were often composed of interwoven floral elements. For a more permanent version, craftsmen reproduced the leaves, berries, and flowers in faience, a glazed ceramic material (Cat. Nos. 20, 21 and 22) easily made and inexpensively priced. Few, however, could have afforded an example as elegant as this gold and carnelian necklace.

The gold and carnelian pendants represent cornflowers (Cat. No. 67), a common and colorful plant in Egyptian gardens. They are accompanied by gold and carnelian disk beads and tiny gold spacer beads. The present stringing in nineteen rows of alternating bead types is based on contemporary New Kingdom models. At the time of their discovery, they were scattered among other precious objects in one of two caches found at ancient Bubastis (Cat. Nos. 49, 67 and 70), a city in the Delta.

Material: Gold and carnelian
Provenance: Bubastis
Width of Present Mounting: 36 cm.
  (14.2 in.)
Date: New Kingdom
Cairo Accession No.: JE 39875 =
  CG 53184
Catalogue References:
  Brigham Young University No. 64
  Montreal and Vancouver No. 27

69

Ewer of King Ahmos

Since the gods of ancient Egypt demanded food and drink as well as clothing, shelter, and amusement on a daily basis, the presentation of liquid offerings played an important role in temple ceremonies. Temple walls frequently depict the reigning king in the act of pouring a libation to the resident god from a vessel similar in shape to this example. It also served as a container for the first flood waters and their accompanying hope for fertility and rebirth (Cat. No. 6).

Although this ewer was found in Tanis in the tomb of the Twenty-first Dynasty king Psusennes I (together with other gold and silver vessels; Cat. Nos. 63-66), it bears the name of the first pharaoh of the Eighteenth Dynasty, Ahmose. King Ahmose is credited with expelling foreign rulers known as the Hyksos from the Delta and restoring native rule to Egypt. The inscription calls Ahmose the good god, beloved of Osiris, lord of Abydos. Since Osiris was a funerary god, the vessel may have been made for Ahmose's tomb.

The neck, spout, body and foot of the jar were hammered separately from sheet gold and then soldered together.

Material: Gold
Provenance: Tanis
Height: 14.6 cm. (5.7 in.)
Max. Diam.: 5 cm. (1.96 in.)
Base Diam.: 4 cm. (1.6 in.)
Date: New Kingdom, Dynasty
  XVIII, Ahmose
Cairo Accession No.: JE 85895
Catalogue References:
  Brigham Young University No. 12
  Montreal and Vancouver No. 25

70
Chalice of Queen Tausert

Skilled artisans have combined the pointed petals of the common blue lotus with the vertical striations of the rarer white lotus on the bowl of this golden drinking vessel. The shape of the vessel's foot and its incised petals recall the umbel of the papyrus plant. Since lotuses flourished in Nile waters and its canals, they became the symbolic flower of the Nile Valley or Upper Egypt. The Delta marshes ideally suited the papyrus plant, which became synonymous with Lower Egypt. Together the two plants signify all Egypt.

Engraved on the foot of the chalice is the cartouche of Queen Tausert, and it is surmounted by a sun disk and double plumes. This was the female crown *par excellence*, popularized by Ramesses II's Great Royal Wife Nefertari and adopted by subsequent Nineteenth Dynasty queens. Little is known about the short reign (two years) of Queen Tausert, the last of Dynasty XIX. After the death of her husbands, Sety II and Siptah, she became the sole ruler of Egypt, the second woman of the New Kingdom (after Hatshepsut) to achieve that distinction.

The cup and foot of the chalice were made separately and soldered together. Like Cat. Nos. 49, 62 and 68, this vessel was part of one of the two Bubastis hoards.

Material: Gold
Provenance: Bubastis
Height: 9.5 cm. (3.7 in.)
Cup Diam.: 8 cm. (3.1 in.)
Base Diam.: 4.3 cm. (1.7 in.)
Date: New Kingdom, Dynasty XIX, Queen Tausert
Cairo Accession No.: JE 39872 = CG 53260
Catalogue References:
Brigham Young University No. 67
Montreal and Vancouver No. 26

71
Ramesses II and the Gods of Armant

In many cities Ramesses II dedicated monuments to local gods. Here the king, attired in royal regalia, clutches two standards featuring the god and goddess of Armant, a city just north of Thebes. At his right side is the falcon-headed Montu, a warrior god, and to his left is Montu's consort, Rat-tawy, shown with a human head and wig surmounted by a sun disk and cow horns. In the column of inscription on each staff, Ramesses II relates that he made this statue as a monument to "his father" Montu and "his mother" Rat-tawy. The standard bearing statue type was especially common during Ramesses II's reign. Placed in front of a temple or inside the first court, in this case at Armant, it would have been available to any passer-by for worship. In that manner it served as an intermediary between god and man.

Every aspect of this statue heralds Ramesses the Great's power and majesty. Over seven feet tall as it is now, a hole on top of the wig indicates that the king once wore a headdress, probably the *atef* crown. With its tall stylized plumes, feathers and a sun disk, the crown could easily have added another three feet. A second base for the statue, still in the courtyard of the Cairo Museum, measures two and one-half feet.

Striding regally forth in the traditional left-foot-forward pose of the Egyptian male figure, the king displays the physique of a trim young man. Chronologically, he was at least in his mid-fifties at the time this statue was commissioned, since the inscription on the base refers to the jubilee festivals he had celebrated. Ramesses II wears the royal uraeus and beard, a beaded collar, and a kilt ornamented with a panther-head apron and pendant uraeii. The panther apron signifies his role as high priest giving service to his god.

Material: Granite
Provenance: Armant
Height: 244 cm. (96.1 in.)
Width: 100 cm. (39.4 in.)
Base: 73 cm. (28.7 in.) x 103 cm. (40.6 in.)
Date: New Kingdom, Dynasty XIX, Ramesses II
Cairo Accession No.: JE 44668
Catalogue References:
Brigham Young University No. 50
Montreal and Vancouver No. 1

72
Column Drum Reinscribed for Ramesses II

In constructing his vast architectural complexes throughout the Delta and Nile Valley, not only did Ramesses the Great quarry new stone, but he also reused his royal ancestors' monuments. King Tuthmosis IV (1425-1417 B.C.) originally erected this channeled column, and his names may still be read on it. However, Ramesses II took it for his own use, and his representation covers far more of the surface area. The king wears the *kheperesh* or warrior crown with a coiled uraeus and two pendant streamers, a beaded necklace, and a royal kilt. In one hand he holds three lotus flowers, symbols of rebirth, and in the other a composite bouquet. The ancient Egyptian word for flowers, *renpeyt,* is similar to *renpey,* to become young, and *renpuwt,* to enjoy many more years. Accordingly, by presenting the gods flowers, he receives in return youth and a long life.

The falcon god Horus, whose talons clutch the *shen-ring* (the hieroglyph meaning "to surround" and "to protect"), hovers above the king. It may also have symbolized rejuvenation. Ramesses II is identified by two of his five names, written in cartouches to the left of his visage. One of these names, the composite *User-Ma'at-Ra Setep-en-Ra,* adopted at his coronation, is also inscribed on his belt.

The practice of reusing older monuments did not stop with Ramesses II. This already twice-used column became part of the foundation of a building erected at the end of the first century A.D. by the Roman emperor Trajan.

Material: Sandstone
Provenance: Elephantine
Height: 162 cm. (63.8 in.)
Diam.: 96 cm. (37.8 in.)
Date: New Kingdom, Dynasties
  XVIII and XIX, Tuthmosis IV and
  Ramesses II
Cairo Accession No.: JE 41560
Catalogue References:
  Brigham Young University No. 1
  Montreal and Vancouver No. 3

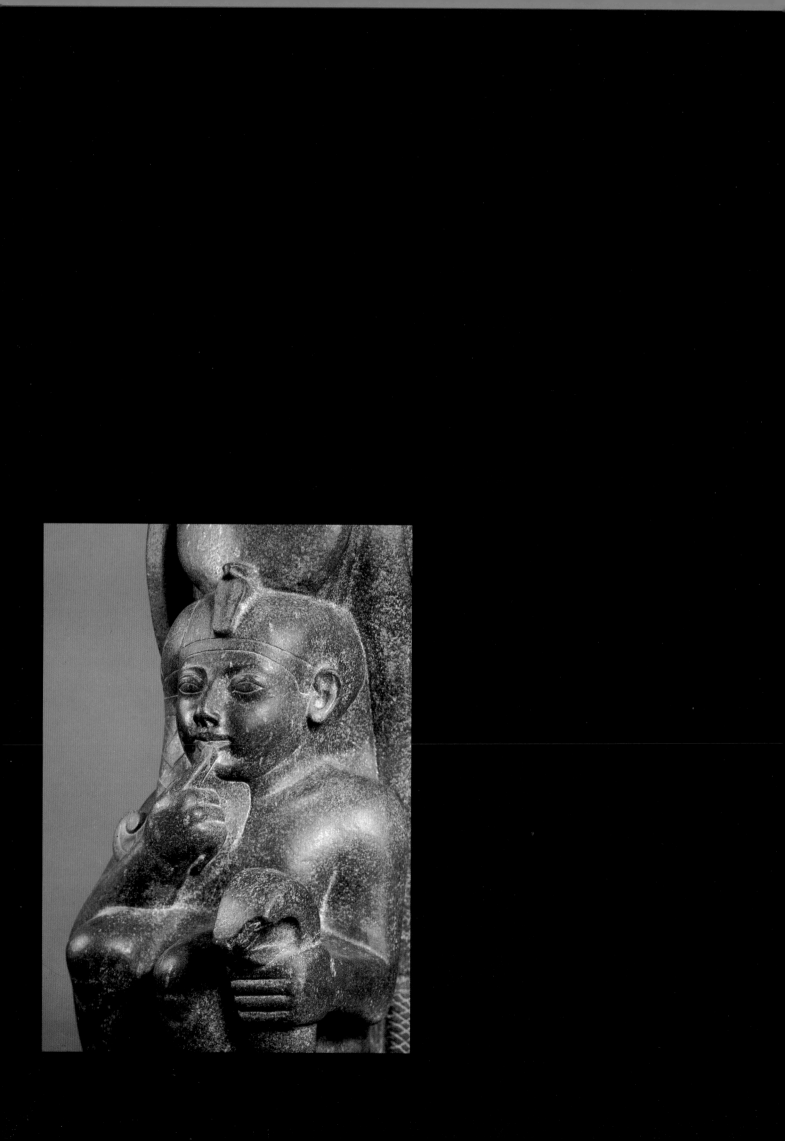

Suggestions for Further Reading

General

Aldred, C. *Egyptian Art* (New York and Toronto, 1980).

Baines, J., and Málek, J. *Atlas of Ancient Egypt* (New York, 1980).

Desroches-Noblecourt, C. *The Great Pharaoh Ramses II and his Time.* An exhibition of antiquities from the Egyptian Museum, Cairo. Palais de la Civilisation, Montréal. June 1-September 29, 1985 (Montreal, 1985).

Edwards, I.E.S. et al., eds. *Cambridge Ancient History, I-III* rev. ed. (Cambridge, 1970-82).

Harris, J.R., ed. *The Legacy of Egypt* (Oxford, 1971).

Hayes, W.C. *The Scepter of Egypt, Part II* (New York, 1959).

James, T.G.H. *An Introduction to Ancient Egypt* (London, 1979).

Kees, H. *Ancient Egypt* (Chicago, 1961).

Mertz, B. *Red Land, Black Land* (New York, 1966).

Sabbahy, L. *Ramses II: The Pharaoh and His Time.* Exhibition Catalog. Brigham Young University. 25 October 1985 to 5 April 1986 (Provo, 1985).

Smith, W.S. *The Art and Architecture of Ancient Egypt* rev. ed. by W.K. Simpson (New York, 1981).

Chapter I—Ramesses the King

Bietak, M. *Avaris and Piramesse: Archaeological Exploration in the Eastern Nile Delta* (London, 1981).

Dimick, M.T. *Memphis, The City of the White Wall* (Philadelphia, 1956).

Gaballa, A. *Narrative in Egyptian Art* (Mainz, 1976).

Gardiner, A. *The Kadesh Inscriptions of Ramesses II* (Oxford, 1960).

Goedicke, H., ed. *Perspectives on the Battle of Kadesh* (Baltimore, 1985).

Hayes, W.C. *Glazed Tiles from a Palace of Ramesses II at Kantir. 1937* (New York, 1973).

Jeffreys, D.G. *The Survey of Memphis I* (London, 1985).

Kitchen, K.A. *Pharaoh Triumphant: The Life and Times of Ramesses II* (Mississauga, Canada, 1982).

Redford, D. *Pharaonic King—Lists, Annals and Day Books: A Contribution to the Egyptian Sense of History* (Mississauga, Canada, 1986).

Yadin, Y. *The Art of Warfare in Biblical Lands in Light of Archaeological Study* (New York, 1963).

Chapter II—Egypt in the Ramesside Age

Alfred, C. *Jewels of the Pharaohs* (London, 1971).

Bietak, M. "Urban Archaeology and the Town Problem in Ancient Egypt," in *Egyptology and the Social Sciences,* ed. K. Weeks (Cairo, 1979), pp. 97-144.

Caminos, R. *Late-Egyptian Miscellanies* (London, 1954).

Cerný, J. *Ancient Egyptian Religion* (London, 1952).

Cerný, J. *Prices and Wages in Egypt in the Ramesside Period* (Paris, 1954).

Egypt's Golden Age: The Art of Living in the New Kingdom 1558-1085 B.C. (Boston, 1982).

Frankfort, H. *Ancient Egyptian Religion, An Interpretation* (New York, 1961).

Foster, J. *Love Songs of the New Kingdom* (New York, 1974).

van der Haagen, J. K. "Rameses' Mysterious Encounter at Dawn at the Great Temple of Abu Simbel," *The Unesco Courier* (October, 1962), pp. 10-15.

Habachi, L. *Features of the Deification of Ramesses II* (Gluckstadt, 1969).

Habachi, L. *The Obelisks of Egypt: Skyscrapers of the Past* (New York, 1977).

James, T. G. H. *Pharaoh's People: Scenes from Life in Imperial Egypt* (London, 1984).

Janssen, J. *Commodity Prices from the Ramesside Period. An Economic Study of the Village of Necropolis Workmen at Thebes* (Leiden, 1975).

Kemp, B. "Imperialism and Empire in New Kingdom Egypt (c. 1575-1087 B.C.)" in *Imperialism in the Ancient World,* eds. Garnsey and Whittaker (Cambridge, 1978), pp. 7-57.

Kitchen, K. A. "From the Brickfields of Egypt," *Tyndale Bulletin* 27 (1976), pp. 137-147.

Lesko, B. *King Tut's Wine Cellar* (Berkeley, 1977).

Lichtheim, M. *Ancient Egyptian Literature: A Book of Readings, Vols. I-III* (Berkeley, 1973-80).

Lucas, A. *Ancient Egyptian Materials and Industries* 4th ed., rev. and enlarged by J. R. Harris (London, 1962).

Montet, P. *Everyday Life in Egypt in the Days of Ramesses the Great.* 1958 (Philadelphia, 1981).

Nims, C. *Thebes of the Pharaohs* (New York, 1965).

O'Conner, D. "The Geography of Settlement in Ancient Egypt," in *Man, Settlement, and Urbanism,* eds. P. Ucko et al. (London, 1972), pp. 681-698.

Redford, D. "Studies in Relations between Palestine and Egypt during the First Millennium B.C. I. The Taxation System of Solomon," in *Studies on the Ancient Palestinian World,* eds. J. Wevers and D. Redford (Toronto, 1972), pp. 141-156.

Riefstahl, E. *Thebes in the Time of Amunhotep III* (Norman, 1964).

Romer, J. *Ancient Lives: Daily Life in Egypt of the Pharaohs* (New York, 1984).

Sauneron, S. *The Priests of Ancient Egypt* (New York, 1960).

Simpson, W. K. ed. *The Literature of Ancient Egypt* (New Haven and London, 1972).

Smith, H. S. "Society and Settlement in Ancient Egypt; in *Man, Settlement, and Urbanism* eds. P. Ucko et al. (London, 1972), pp. 705-719.

Trigger, B. G. et al. *Ancient Egypt: A Social History* (Cambridge, 1983).

Chapter III—Quest for Immortality

Andrews, C. *Egyptian Mummies* (London, 1984).

Balout, L., Robert, C. and Desroches-Noblecourt, C., et al. *La Momie de Ramses II* (Paris, 1985), includes English abstract.

Bierbrier, M. *The Tomb Builders of the Pharaohs* (London, 1982).

Cerný, J. *A Community of Workmen at Thebes in the Ramesside Period* (Cairo, 1973).

Edwards, A. *A Thousand Miles up the Nile.* 1891 (Los Angeles, 1983).

Fagan, B. *The Rape of the Nile* (New York, 1975).

Greener, L. *High Dam over Nubia* (New York, 1962).

Harris, J. E., and Weeks, K. *X-Raying the Pharaohs* (London, 1973).

MacQuitty, W. *Abu Simbel* (London, 1965).

Mekhitarian, A. *Egyptian Painting* (Geneva, 1978).

Romer, J. *Valley of the Kings* (New York, 1981).

Index

Photographers

Jon Abbott
pp. vi-vii, 21, 22-23, 24-25 bottom, 27 lower right, 30, 33, 35 middle and bottom, 37 top, 38-39, 41, 43, 47, 48 top, 50-51, 52, 54 top and bottom, 56 upper left, 57 bottom, 58, 59 top, 60, 61, 62-63, 64, 66 lower right, 67, 68-69, 70-71, 72, 73, 74, 75 top, 76 top, 77 middle left, 78 top, 79, 80, 86, 87, 89 top and bottom, 94-95, 96, 97, 98, 99, 100-101, 102 top, 107 upper left, upper right, bottom, 108, 109 bottom, 111, 112 right, 114, 119, 120-121, 123

Sharon Avery
p. 5 lower right

Glen A. Campbell
pp. 2 upper left and right, 3 upper right and bottom, 4 lower left and lower right, 5 upper left and lower left, 7, 10

William Eggleston (Memphis Brooks Museum of Art Collection)
pp. 12-13, 14-15, 16, 17, 18-19, 20

Rita E. Freed
pp. 37 bottom, 75 middle left, 88

Kenneth S. Graetz, City of Montreal
cover, pp. ii, 129, 131-133, 135-137, 139, 141-145, 147, 149-151, 153-155, 157-159, 161-189, 191-201, 203-208

Margaret Nutt Moore
pp. 2 lower left and lower right, 4 upper right

Gary Richardson
p. 90 upper left

Institutions

The British Museum
pp. 25 upper, 55, 116 top

The Brooklyn Museum
pp. 31, 56 bottom, 78 bottom, 102 bottom (photographed by David Loggie for The Brooklyn Museum Mut Expedition), 104 (photographed by David Loggie for The Brooklyn Museum Mut Expedition), 105 (photographed by David Loggie for The Brooklyn Museum Mut Expedition), 106, 112 left

Center of Documentation and Studies on Ancient Egypt (C.E.D.A.E.)
pp. 27 upper left (Neg. 16879), 40 (Neg. 12263), 42 (Neg. 10638), 48 middle (Neg. 6865), 53 top (Neg. 8567), 65 upper right (Neg. 13233), middle left (Neg. 12139), 66 upper left (Neg. 10603), 84 (Neg. 11777), 116 bottom (Neg. 16968)

Cleveland Museum of Art
p. 103 (Gift of the John Huntington Art and Polytechnic Trust)

Egypt Exploration Society—Rijksmuseum van Oudheden, Leiden Expedition to the New Kingdom Necropolis at Saqqara
p. 45

Egyptian Antiquities Organization
p. 1

Manning/Ciani-Kaiser
pp. 3 upper left, 4 upper left

Manning/Pleskow
pp. 28 upper left, upper right, bottom, 46, 90 upper right, 92, 109 top

The Metropolitan Museum of Art, New York
pp. 85, 93 (Egyptian Expedition of The Metropolitan Museum of Art Rogers Fund, 1930)

Courtesy Dr. Gamal Mokhtar, Egyptian Antiquities Organization, Cairo
p. 53 lower, 117

Musee du Louvre, Paris
pp. 56 upper right, 76 bottom, 81

Musei Vaticani
p. 26

Museo Egizio, Turin (Chomon-Perino Photograph)
pp. 24 left, 32, 59 middle, 77 bottom

Pelizaeus-Museum, Hildesheim
pp. 35 top, 57 top

Staatliche Sammlung Agyptischer Kunst, Munich
p. 82 (photo by Dietrich Wildung)